Now I Know! 2

Workbook

Cheryl Pelteret

Contents

1	What do we do on school days?	Page 4
2	Where do wild animals live?	Page 18
3	How does the weather change?	Page 32
4	What can you find in big cities?	Page 46
5	How do we celebrate?	Page 60
6	What jobs can I do?	Page 74
7	Why do we play sports?	Page 88
8	What makes us feel good?	Page 102
9	How are the seasons different?	Page 116
10	How are we all different?	Page 130
11	How do we solve problems?	Page 144
12	Why is it good to be outdoors?	Page 158

1 What do we do on school days?

What do you know?

1 What do you learn about in this unit? Read and complete.

We learn about what we do at .... on different days.

2 🎬 1-1 BBC Watch the video. Read and match.

1 There's reading   a on Tuesday.
2 Football is   b on Sunday.
3 Computer games are   c on Saturday.
4 Music homework is   d on Friday.
5 The piano lesson is   e every day.

3 Write the missing letters. Then number in the correct order.

DAYS of the week!

○ W__d__e__d____ __
○ Su__d__ __y
○ F__ __ d__ __y
① M__ __ d__ __
○ S__ __ __ __ d__ __y
○ T__u__ __d__ __y
○ T__ __e__ __da__

4 What about you? Read and check (✓).

1 I go to school on
   Monday ☐   Friday ☐
   Tuesday ☐   Saturday ☐
   Wednesday ☐   Sunday ☐
   Thursday ☐

2 I stay at home on
   Monday ☐   Friday ☐
   Tuesday ☐   Saturday ☐
   Wednesday ☐   Sunday ☐
   Thursday ☐

Vocabulary 1

1 🎧 01 📋 Listen and check (✓).

1 What class does Pat have today?

a  ☐   b  ☐   c ☐

2 What's Nick's favorite class?

a  ☐   b  ☐   c ☐

3 What does Lucy have on Fridays?

a  ☐   b  ☐   c ☐

2 Look and write.

1 ___ ___ ___

2 ___ ___ ___ ___ ___ ___ ___
  science

3 ___ ___ ___

4 ___ ___ ___ ___ practice

5 ___ ___ ___ ___

3 Write the letters in order. Which schedule is Ben's? Check (✓).

Today I have r / a / t _____ ,
i / o / l / v / i / n _____ practice,
and e / r / p / u / t / m / o / c _____ science.

a ☐   b ☐

4 Draw and write about your classes today. What's your favorite class?

Today I have _____ .

Word study: c and s

5 Circle the letter c where it sounds like an s in the following words.

1 practice
2 face
3 science
4 juice

6 Look at Activity 5. Write the words in alphabetical order.

6

Reading 1

1 Read *Billy the Dragon*. Number the sentences in the correct order.

- _1_ Billy's friends go to school.
- ___ Billy's friends come home from school.
- ___ Billy runs and jumps.
- ___ Billy plays the drums.
- ___ They draw in art.
- ___ Billy likes being with his friends.

2 Read *Billy the Dragon* again and match.

1. Billy doesn't
2. Billy draws
3. Billy counts
4. Billy doesn't have
5. Billy plays

a   the drums.
b   go to school.
c   his toes.
d   piano practice.
e   a flower.

3 Read, choose, and write.

> classes   draw   his friends
> P.E.   piano

1. Billy's friends have six _____ today.
2. They _____ in art.
3. They run and jump in _____.
4. Billy doesn't have a _____ or a violin.
5. Billy likes being with _____.

4 What about you? Read and circle.

1. I **like** / **don't like** being with my friends.
2. I'm **happy** / **sad** at school.
3. I **have** / **don't have** a piano.
4. I **play the drums** / **learn a lot of new things** at school.
5. I **have** / **don't have** math on Wednesdays.

7

Grammar 1

I **don't go** to school.
He **plays** the drums.
We **run** in P.E.
They **don't count** in art.

1 Read and circle.

1 **Eva:** I ¹ **like / likes** math and English.
   Tom: English is fun. But I ² **doesn't / don't** like math.
             We ³ **draw / draws** pictures in art. It's my favorite class.
   Eva: My favorite class is P.E. but we ⁴ **don't / doesn't** have P.E. today.

2 **Pablo:** I ⁵ **walk / walks** to school. What about you?
   Freya: I ⁶ **go / goes** by bus. May ⁷ **go / goes** by car.

2 Write the words in order.

1 I / like / P.E. / don't ....
2 We / jump / math / in / don't ....
3 doesn't / school / to / A dragon / go ....
4 Today / violin / I / practice / have ....
5 doesn't / the drums / play / My teacher ....

3 Read and write the opposite.

1 I like science. *I don't like science.*
2 You have a violin. ....
3 My friend walks to school. ....
4 My teacher goes to school by car. ....
5 We play tennis after school. ....
6 My friends run and jump in P.E. ....

4 Look, read, and write.

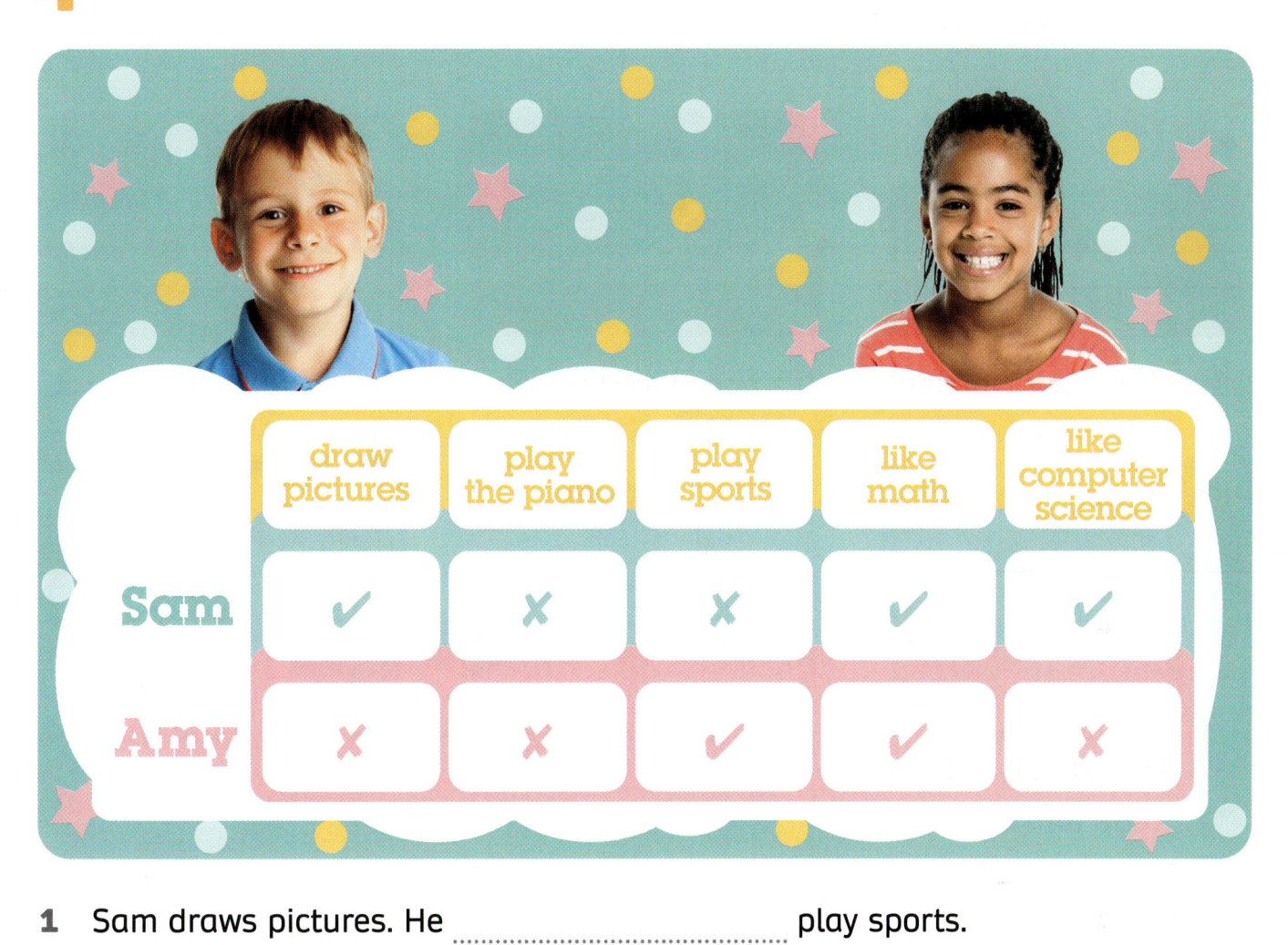

	draw pictures	play the piano	play sports	like math	like computer science
Sam	✓	✗	✗	✓	✓
Amy	✗	✗	✓	✓	✗

1 Sam draws pictures. He _____ play sports.
2 Amy _____ like computer science.
3 Amy and Sam _____ play the piano.
4 Sam _____ computer science.
5 Amy _____ draw pictures.
6 Sam and Amy _____ math.

5 Write for you. Use the words from Activity 4.

1 I don't draw pictures.
2
3
4
5

Vocabulary 2

1 Look, read, and circle.

1. It's **difficult** / **worried**.
2. It's **easy** / **busy**.
3. It's **bored** / **interesting**.
4. I'm **worried** / **tired**.
5. I'm **bored** / **important**.
6. It's **easy!** / **I'm worried**.

2 Read and circle.

1. Sorry, I can't help you now. I'm very **important** / **busy**.
2. I can't play this music. It's very **difficult** / **easy**.
3. I don't like this book. **It isn't interesting.** / **It's busy**.
4. I want to go to bed. I'm **tired** / **important**.
5. Do your homework! **It's important.** / **I'm worried**.

3 Read, choose, and write.

| bored | difficult | easy | interesting | not worried |

1. I know all my new words for my test today. I'm _____.
2. I have nothing to do. I'm _____.
3. I can't do this math. It's _____.
4. P.E. is my favorite class. It's _____.
5. I can spell C A T. It's _____.

4 Find and circle eight words.

bored
busy
easy
difficult
important
interesting
tired
worried

I	N	T	E	R	E	S	T	I	N	G
H	O	I	J	K	A	U	C	R	Y	I
B	O	R	E	D	S	B	U	S	Y	O
A	B	E	U	W	Y	P	H	A	T	E
W	O	D	I	F	F	I	C	U	L	T
I	M	P	O	R	T	A	N	T	A	S
P	U	D	T	W	O	R	R	I	E	D

Vocabulary challenge: relaxed, excited, angry

5 Look, read, and circle.

1 excited / angry

2 angry / relaxed

3 excited / relaxed

6 Read and write. Use the words from Activity 5.

1 When my team loses a game, I feel _____.
2 I have soccer practice after school today. I'm _____.
3 I don't have any homework to do. I feel _____.

11

Reading 2

1 Read *After School*. Circle **T** (true) or **F** (false).

1 We jump in karate and gymnastics.   T   F
2 We wear shoes in karate.   T   F
3 We play games in drama class.   T   F
4 We're bored in gymnastics.   T   F
5 We don't dance and sing in karate.   T   F

2 Read *After School* again and match.

1 We put chalk   a in the legs or face.
2 We're always busy   b in karate and drama class.
3 We listen to our friends   c in gymnastics.
4 We don't kick people   d after karate.
5 I'm tired   e on our hands and feet.

3 What do you do in your favorite after-school class? Draw and write.

My favorite after-school class is _____ .
In this class, I _____ .
We always _____ .
We don't _____ .

12

Grammar 2

> **Do** you play the piano?   **Yes**, I **do**.
> **Do** you and your friends go to gymnastics after school?   **No**, we **don't**.
> **Do** your friends like math?   **Yes**, they **do**.
> **Does** he go to karate class?   **No**, he **doesn't**.
> **Does** she play the piano?   **Yes**, she **does**.

1 Read and check (✓).

1. Do you do karate on Mondays?   Yes, she does. ☐   No, I don't. ☐
2. Does your sister have a bike?   Yes, she does. ☐   Yes, he does. ☐
3. Does your father drive a car?   No, he doesn't. ☐   Yes, I do. ☐
4. Do you and your sister have piano practice after school?   Yes, they do. ☐   Yes, we do. ☐
5. Do your friends walk to school?   No, I don't. ☐   Yes, they do. ☐

2 Read and circle.

1. **Do** / **Does** you get up early in the morning?
2. **Do** / **Does** you and your friends read books?
3. **Do** / **Does** your sister do gymnastics after school?
4. **Do** / **Does** your parents speak English?
5. **Do** / **Does** your brother watch TV in the morning?

3 Look at Activity 2. Write for you.

1. ....
2. ....
3. ....
4. ....
5. ....

4 Read and write *do* or *does*.

1. .... you like those flowers, Miss Brown?

Yes, I 2 ....

3 .... you like learning new things, children?

SCIENCE EXPERIMENT

Yes, we 4 .... !

5 .... a flower need water?

Yes, it 6 .... !

Look! The water's blue. 7 .... the flowers drink the blue water?

Yes, they 8 ....

9 .... the flower change color, Miss Brown?

Let's look at the flower tomorrow!

THE NEXT DAY

14

Writing

1 Read Ben's schedule. Write sentences with *and*.

> **Remember**
> 1 Read.
> 2 Get ready to write.
> 3 Now write!

Monday

In the morning: English, art

In the afternoon: science, P.E.

After school: have piano practice, do karate

At home: watch TV, do my homework, go to sleep!

On Mondays, I have two classes in the morning ¹ **and** two classes in the afternoon. In the morning, I have English ² .... In the afternoon, I have ³ .... After school, I have ⁴ .... Then I go home. At home, I watch TV, ⁵ .... !

2 Choose a school day. Complete the chart for you.

Day: ....

In the morning	In the afternoon	After school	At home

3 Write about your schedule for one day. Use your notes from Activity 2.

On .... , I have ....

....

in the morning. In the afternoon, ...

....

....

15

Now I Know

1 Look at Tina's schedule for Thursday. Read, choose, and write.

> art   computer science   math   music
> science   violin practice

	Morning	Afternoon	After school
Thursday	art, music, computer science	science, math	violin

On Thursday, Tina has ¹ _____
in the morning. In the afternoon, she has ² _____ and
_____. After school, Tina has ³ _____.

2 Read and circle.

Kate: ¹ **Do** / **Does** you like science?

Pedro: Yes, I ² **do** / **does**, but it isn't easy.
        It's ³ **difficult** / **busy**.

Kate: Yes, but it's very ⁴ **bored** / **important**.

Pedro: I ⁵ **like** / **likes** English a lot. I'm never
        ⁶ **interesting** / **bored** in my English
        class. I'm always ⁷ **easy** / **happy**.

Paula: ⁸ **Do** / **Does** you and your friends
        sing in the English class?

Amit: No, we ⁹ **doesn't** / **don't**. We sing
        in our drama class!

Paula: ¹⁰ **Do** / **Does** your teacher laugh
        and jump in drama class?

Amit: Yes, she ¹¹ **do** / **does**!

3 Read, choose, and write.

> count   don't   experiments   interesting
> karate   learn   run   speak   tired

We ¹ _____ a lot of new things at school. We ² _____ in math, and we do ³ _____ in science. Science is very ⁴ _____. We ⁵ _____ English in our English class. We listen to the teacher, and we ⁶ _____ talk. We shout and kick in ⁷ _____, and we ⁸ _____ a lot in P.E. I'm always ⁹ _____ after P.E.

Things I learn

1 What do you do and learn at school? Write six words.

....
....

2 My new words! Draw and write.

3 My favorite words in this unit!

My three favorite words in this unit are _____.

2 Where do wild animals live?

What do you know?

1 What do you learn about in this unit? Read and complete.

We learn facts about .... animals and where they ....

2 🎬 2-1 BBC Watch the video. Read, choose, and write.

> feet   fish   flowers   grass   teeth   trees

1 In the forest I can see a lot of ....
2 A bear catches a ....
3 There's a lot of green .... in the savannah.
4 A kangaroo has big ....
5 In the jungle there are a lot of ....
6 Tigers have very big ....

3 🎬 2-1 BBC Look, choose, and write. Watch the video again to check.

> forest   jungle   outback   savannah

1   2   3   4

4 Where does each animal live? Look at Activity 3 and draw.

> a bear   an elephant   a kangaroo   a tiger

18

Vocabulary 1

1 Look and write the letters in order.

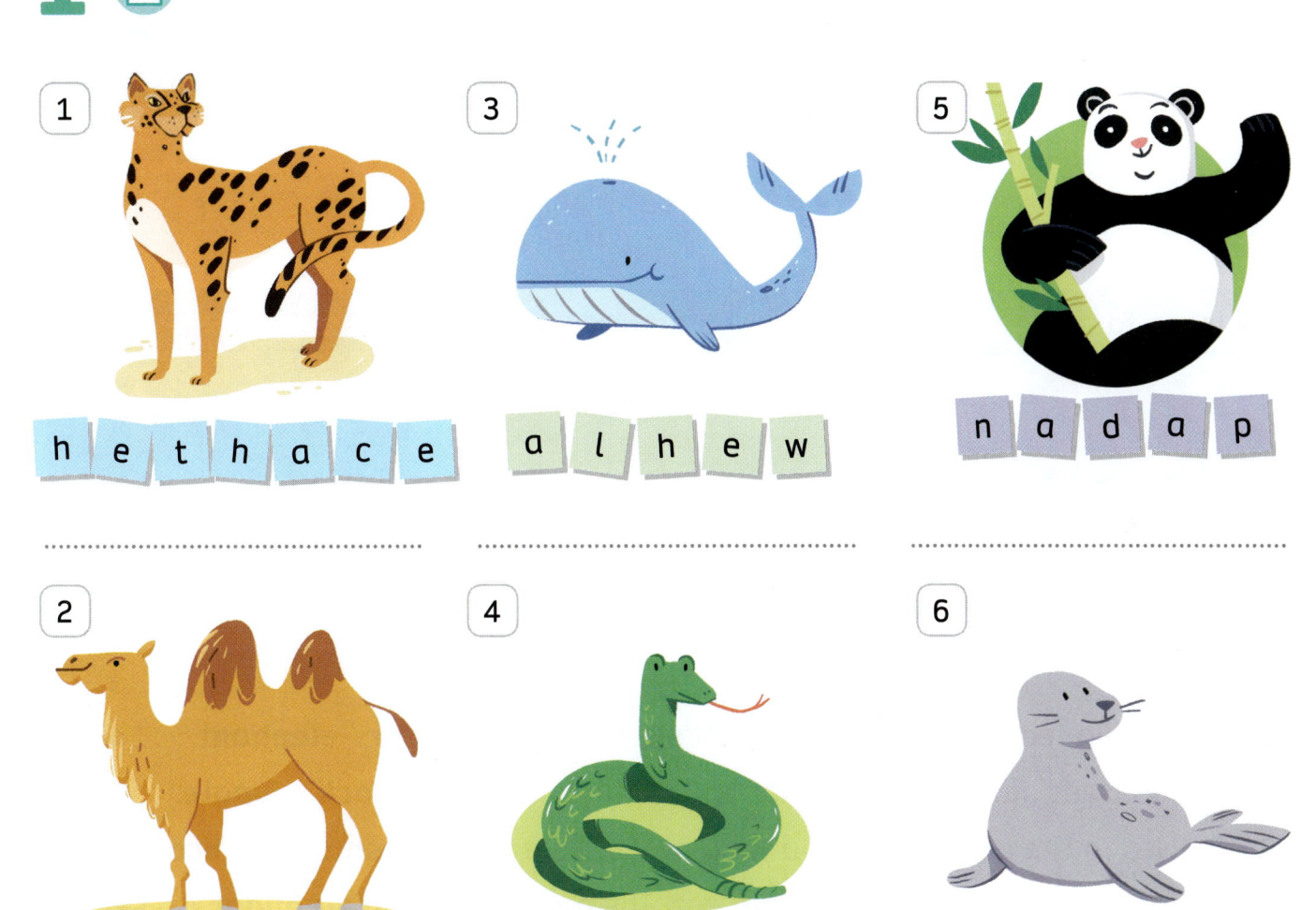

1. h e t h a c e
2. m e c a l
3. a l h e w
4. n e s a k
5. n a d a p
6. l a s e

2 Read and match.

1. A camel lives
2. A snake
3. A cheetah is
4. A seal and a whale swim
5. A panda lives
6. A crocodile has
7. A kangaroo can

a. doesn't have legs.
b. in the ocean.
c. big teeth.
d. in the desert.
e. jump high.
f. a big cat.
g. in the forest.

3 Where do these animals live? Look and write.

1. d ....
3. r ....
5. b ....
   m .... f ....
2. o ....
4. s ....
6. j ....

4 Read and circle.

1. It has big feet. It can jump high. It's a **seal / kangaroo / elephant**.
2. It has trees, flowers, and animals. It's the **ocean / outback / jungle**.
3. It lives in the desert. It has a long neck. It's a **camel / snake / crocodile**.
4. It has four legs, but it isn't a big cat. It's **a cheetah / an elephant / a seal**.
5. It's hot and dry. There aren't a lot of trees. It's the **jungle / river / desert**.

Word study: the sound h

5 Write the missing letters.

1. zebr___
2. koal___
3. ___ippo
4. iguan___
5. ___edgehog
6. savann___h
7. pand___
8. cheeta___
9. ___amster

6 Look at Activity 5. In which words do we say the sound *h*? In which words is *h* silent? Circle the words with a silent *h*.

Reading 1

1 Read *Max and Mandy's Adventure!* Look at the map and number the places they visit in the correct order.

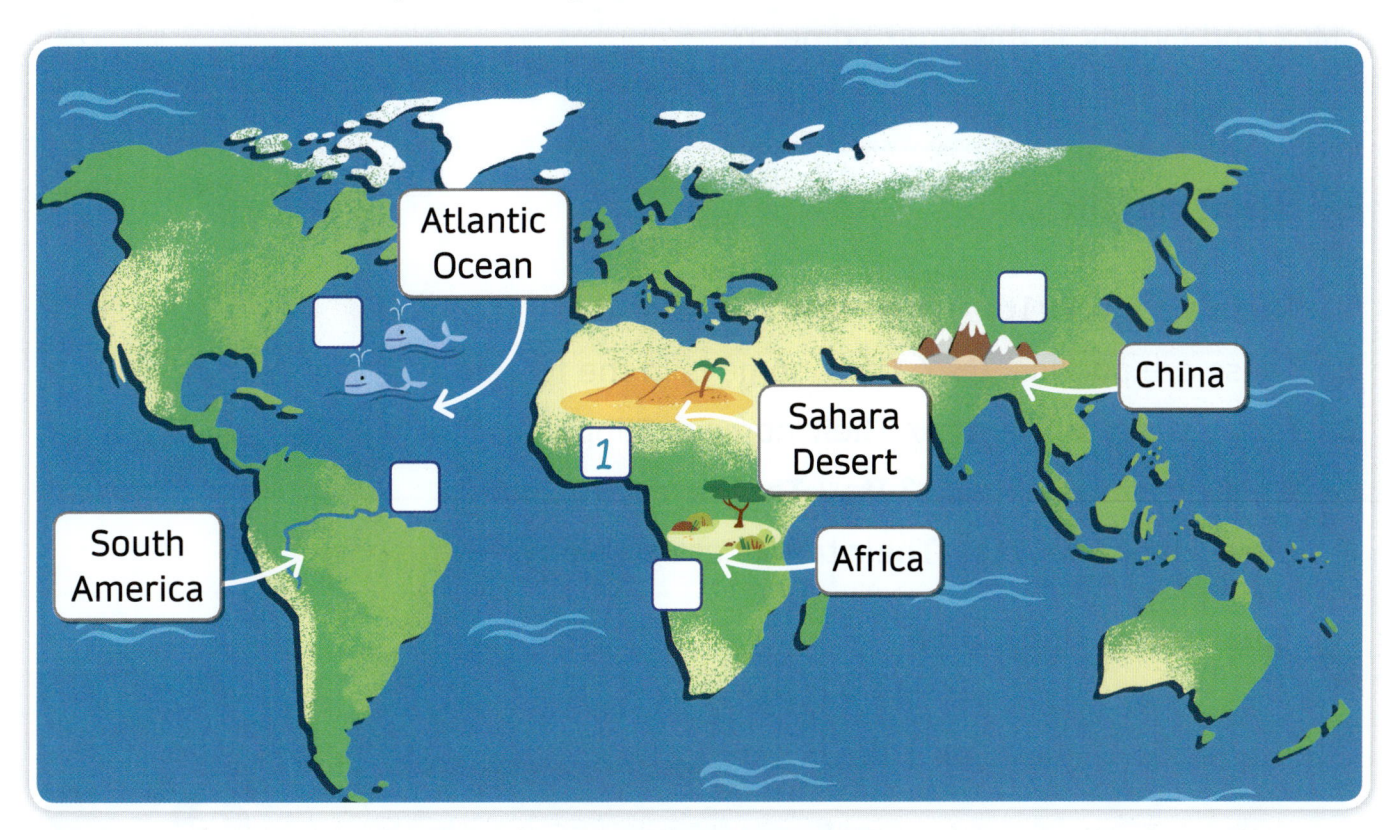

2 Read *Max and Mandy's Adventure!* again and circle **T** (true) or **F** (false).

1. Camels have small heads.   T   F
2. Pandas live in China.   T   F
3. Crocodiles have short legs.   T   F
4. Whales have small bodies.   T   F
5. Cheetahs have big heads.   T   F

3 Think and write.

1. Do you like pictures of animals? ....
2. Do you think it's easy to take pictures of wild animals? ....
3. Which wild animals would you like to take pictures of? ....

....

21

Grammar 1

> The crocodile has big teeth. **Its** teeth are big!
> The camels have long legs. **Their** legs are long.
> Max and Mandy, is this **your** camera?
> Yes! This is **our** camera!

1 Read and circle.

1 There's a hippo. **Its / Their** teeth are big.
2 These are pandas. **Its / Their** home is in the forest.
3 I have a pet snake! **Its / Their** name is Slippy.
4 What are those animals? **Its / Their** eyes are small.
5 I love elephants. **Its / Their** trunks are so funny.

2 Look, read, and match.

a   c   e
b   d   f

1 Its legs are long. Its hair is black and white. [f]
2 Their bodies are long. Their legs are short, and their teeth are big. ☐
3 Its head is small. Its tail is long, and its eyes are small. ☐
4 Their bodies are long. Their eyes are small. Their mouths aren't open. ☐
5 Their heads are white, and their ears are black. ☐
6 Its head and body are big. Its mouth is open, and its teeth are big. ☐

3 Read and write *its*, *their*, *your*, or *our*.

Teacher: Are these ¹ _your_ pictures?
Jane and Sam: Yes, they are. They're pictures of ² _____ trip to the zoo! There are hippos in the river. ³ _____ heads and mouths are so big.
Teacher: I can see crocodiles in the river, too. ⁴ _____ teeth are big.
Jane and Sam: Look at the elephant! ⁵ _____ trunk is so long.
Teacher: Yes. Elephants drink water with ⁶ _____ trunks.
Jane and Sam: This is ⁷ _____ favorite picture. It's very funny.
Teacher: Oh, no! The elephant is eating ⁸ _____ ice cream!

4 Read and write *its* or *their*.

Kangaroos live in the outback. ¹ _Their_ food is grass, flowers, and leaves. ² _____ ears are long, and ³ _____ feet are big. A kangaroo's baby lives in ⁴ _____ pouch.

5 Think of a wild animal. Write about it using *its* and the words in the box.

> ears   feet   hair   head   legs   tail   teeth

My animal is a _____ . It lives _____ .
Its _____ .
Its _____ .

23

Vocabulary 2

1 Look, read, and circle.

1. What a **smart** / **fat** monkey!

2. The bear is very **funny** / **angry**.

3. The elephant is **thin** / **funny**!

4. What a **lazy** / **smart** crocodile.

5. What a **strong** / **lazy** bear.

6. Don't touch it! It's a **funny** / **dangerous** snake.

2 Read and write.

1 I'm a very small mouse. I don't eat a lot. I'm not fat. I'm t_____ .

2 An elephant can carry a tree in its trunk. It's very s_____ .

3 Crocodiles are d_____ . They can eat you.

4 You know all the answers! You're very s_____ .

5 Don't go close to the hippo. It looks a_____ .

3 Read, choose, and write. How would you answer the lion?

~~fat~~   funny   lazy   small

It's a hot and sunny day in the jungle. A ¹ _fat_ lion feels ² _____ . So, he sleeps for an hour. A ³ _____ mouse walks up. "I will pull the lion's tail," she thinks. "It will be ⁴ _____ !"

angry   smart   strong   thin

The lion wakes up. He's ⁵ _____ at the mouse. "That wasn't very ⁶ _____ !" he roars. "I will eat you!" "Don't eat me," says the mouse. "I am only small and ⁷ _____ . A big, ⁸ _____ lion like you needs a bigger meal." "Ok," says the lion. "What should I eat?"

Vocabulary challenge: animal world

4 Look, choose, and write.

claw   paw   roar   zookeeper

1 ....   2 ....   3 ....   4 ....

5 Read and write. Use the words from Activity 4.

1 A _____ works in a zoo.
2 A lion has _____ on his four _____ .
3 When a lion is angry, he _____ !

25

Reading 2

1 Read *In the Wild* and match.

1 Meerkats   a is long and thin.
2 A meerkat's tail   b is hard.
3 Lizards   c aren't funny.
4 Hyenas   d are green, pink, or yellow.
5 An armadillo's body e are funny.

2 Read *In the Wild* again and write.

1 Armadillos and _____ are gray.
2 _____ and armadillos live in South America.
3 _____ have short tails.
4 Meerkats eat _____ .
5 Armadillos don't live in _____ countries.
6 Lizards live in _____ countries.

3 Think and write.

1 What noises do meerkats and hyenas make?

....

2 Do you know any other animal noises? Write about them.

....

3 Why do some lizards change color?

....

26

Grammar 2

How **many** legs does it have? **It doesn't have** legs.
How **big** is it? **It's** not very big. It's small.
How dangerous is it? **It's** very dangerous.

1 Read and write.

1 **Maria:** How smart is an armadillo?
   Joe: An armadillo is very smart!

2 **Sam:** _____ a lizard?
   Tony: A lizard is not dangerous.

3 **Oli:** _____ an armadillo's tail?
   Dina: An armadillo's tail is very long.

4 **Emma:** _____ an elephant?
   Mike: An elephant is very strong.

2 Write the words in order to make questions.

1 rare / butterfly / is / How / this _____ ?
2 big / a / whale / is / How _____ ?
3 fat / How / is / a / hippo _____ ?
4 dangerous / crocodile / a / is / How _____ ?
5 lizard / lazy / is / a / How _____ ?

3 Look at Activity 2 and write the answers. Use *very*.

1 It's very rare.
2 _____
3 _____
4 _____
5 _____

27

> The meerkats are small **and** funny.   Hyenas run **and** chase zebras.

4 Read and match.

1 Pandas are black
2 Lizards live in Europe, Africa,
3 I can see butterflies in the zoo
4 Hyenas live in forests

a and the yard.
b and mountains.
c and South America.
d and white.

5 Write sentences with *and*.

1 A monkey's tail is (long / thin).
   A monkey's tail is long and thin.

2 Lizards are (small / lazy).
   ....

3 Kangaroos can (jump / kick).
   ....

4 Deserts are (hot / dry).
   ....

6 Choose two facts for each animal. Write sentences with *and*.

> are big   are dangerous   are funny   are gray   ~~eat grass~~
> have long noses   have long tails   ~~live in forests~~

1 Pandas *live in forests and eat grass* .
2 Cheetahs ....
3 Meerkats ....
4 Armadillos ....

7 Think and write two facts about yourself. Use *and*.

> am   eat   have   like

1 ....
2 ....

Writing

Remember
1. Read.
2. Get ready to write.
3. Now write!

1 Read, choose, and write.

> angry   big   small   well

Crocodiles swim ¹ .... They have ² .... mouths and sharp teeth. Their ears are ³ .... but they can hear very well. An ⁴ .... crocodile is very dangerous!

2 Complete the chart. Use the words in the box.

> big   black and white   dangerous   forest   lazy
> long legs   ocean   savannah   strong

Animal	Home	Describing words

3 Draw a picture of a wild animal. Then write about it. Use the words from Activity 2.

My favorite animal is a ....

It lives in the ....

It is ....

....

Now I Know

1 Find six animal words. Then complete the chart.

itaelephantbvnkangarooqrypandalotmeerkatecwhalexopcrocodile

in the river	in the desert	in the forest	in the outback	in the ocean	in the savannah

2 Look, choose two words, and write.

angry   big   black   fat   funny   gray   lazy
~~long~~   orange   smart   strong   ~~thin~~

1. A lizard's tail *is long and thin*.

2. This lion _____.

3. An elephant's foot _____.

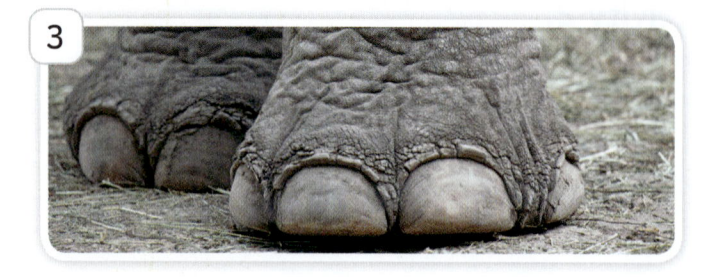

4. A monkey _____.

5. A tiger's body _____.

6. This panda _____.

3 Write the question. Then complete the answers with *is very* or *are very*.

1. beautiful / a butterfly?
   How beautiful is a butterfly?   A butterfly .... beautiful.

2. dangerous / some snakes?
   ....   Some snakes .... dangerous.

4 Read, choose, and write.

its   our   ~~their~~   your

Pandas live in the forest. They find ¹ *their* food in the forest. A camel lives in the desert. It can carry water in ² .... hump. ³ .... class's favorite animal is the lion. It lives in the savannah. What's ⁴ .... favorite animal?

Things I learn

1. **What do you know about wild animals? Write two facts.**

   ....

2. **My new words! Draw and write.**

3. **My favorite words in this unit!**

My three favorite words in this unit are ....

31

3 How does the weather change?

What do you know?

1 What do you learn about in this unit? Read and complete.

We learn about the .... outside and the .... we wear.

2 🎬 3-1 BBC Watch the video. Read and circle.

1 Max is wearing a **sweater / T-shirt**.
2 Kitty is wearing **a dress / pants**.
3 The water is very **hot / cold**.
4 The ice is very **hot / cold**.

3 🎬 3-1 BBC Watch the video again. Number the sentences in the correct order.

4 What's the weather like in your town/city today? Draw and write.

.... Kitty is putting the bowl on the vase.
.... Kitty is putting the ice in the bowl.
.... It's raining!
.... Kitty is taking the ice out of the bag.
..1.... Kitty is pouring the hot water into the vase.
.... It's a cloud.

It's ....

Vocabulary 1

1 Read and circle.

1 Listen to that loud noise! It's **thunder / lightning**!
2 In a big **storm / sleet**, there's wind, rain, thunder, and lightning.
3 It's very **foggy / windy** today. Let's fly a kite!
4 I can't see anything in this **windy / foggy** weather.
5 **Thunder / Sleet** is cold and wet.
6 **Lightning / A tornado** is a very strong wind.
7 Small balls of ice are falling from the sky. It's **thunder / hail**!
8 **Lightning / Sleet** is a bright light in the sky.

2 Look, read, and circle T (true) or F (false). Then write the correct word.

Monday: foggy
Tuesday: sleet
Wednesday: storm
Thursday: thunder and lightning
Friday: hail

1 It's Monday today. It's windy. T F
....

2 It's Tuesday today. There's hail. T F
....

3 It's Wednesday today. There's a storm. T F
....

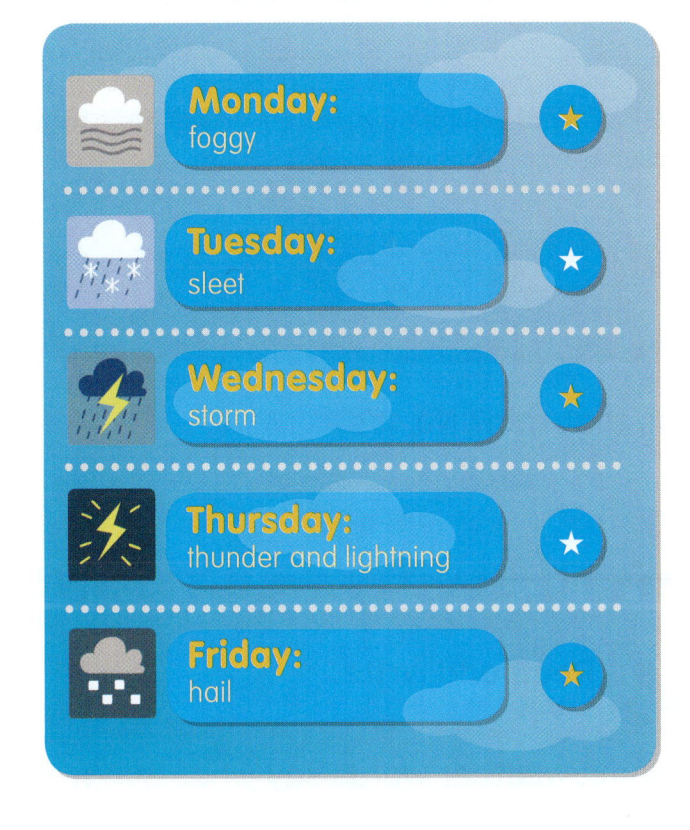

4 It's Thursday. There's thunder and lightning. T F
....

5 It's Friday. There's sleet. T F
....

3 Look, read, and write.

1. Is there lightning? No, there's _sleet_ !

2. Is there thunder? No, there's a _____.

3. Is that rain? No, it's _____ !

4. Is that a light in the sky? No, it's _____ !

5. Is it cloudy? No, it's _____.

6. Is it sunny? No, it's _____.

Word study: weather words ending in -y

4 Read and write.

Some weather words say what things are like: *cloudy*, *windy*, *sunny*. The last letter in these words is _____.

Some weather words say what there is: *there's a storm*, *there's hail*.

5 Circle the weather words ending in -y.

windy   storm   hail   foggy   lightning   sunny

Reading 1

1 Read *The Water Cycle*. Number the sentences in the correct order.

.... The rain falls into the ocean, and the cycle starts again.

.... The vapor changes and becomes a cloud.

... 1 ... The sun makes the water in the ocean hot.

.... The rain falls onto the earth, trees, and grass.

.... The water in the ocean goes up into the air and becomes vapor.

.... Water vapor makes the cloud heavy, and it starts to rain.

2 Look at Activity 1. Number the pictures in the correct order.

3 💡 Why do we need rain? Think and write.

We need rain for plants and grass.

....

....

35

Grammar 1

> **It's** rainy / sunny / foggy / stormy / cloudy / windy.

1 What's the weather like? Read and write.

1. There's fog. *It's foggy.*
2. There's a storm. ....
3. Look at the sun! ....
4. There's a lot of wind. ....
5. There's rain today. ....
6. There are clouds. ....

2 What's the weather like around the world? Look and write.

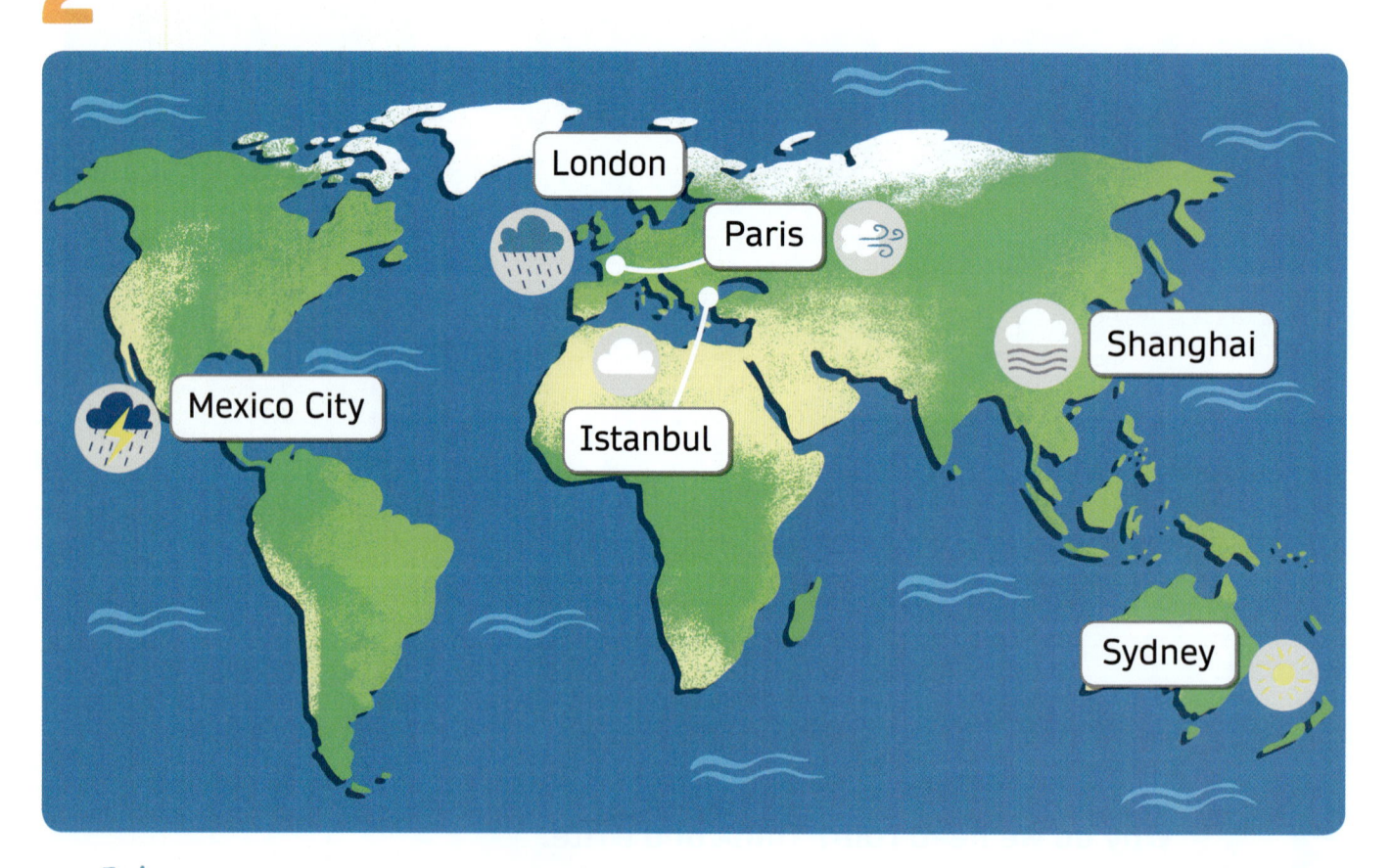

1. *It's rainy* in London.
2. .... in Shanghai.
3. .... in Sydney.
4. .... in Mexico City.
5. .... in Istanbul.
6. .... in Paris.

36

Hot.
Too hot!

Cold.
Too cold!

3 Look, choose, and write.

It's too hot!   ~~It's too cold!~~   It's too cloudy!
It's nice and hot.   It's too windy!

1. I can't swim. It's too cold!

2. Oh, no! ....

3. Mmm. ....

4. I can't see the plane. ....

5. Phew! ....

37

Vocabulary 2

1 Find and circle eight clothes words.

botsneakersindsweatsuitexcaploflipflopsokascarfinsunglassesteryrobeungslippers

2 Complete the chart. Use the words from Activity 1.

On your head	On your feet	Around your neck	On your body

3 Look, read, and circle.

Tina

Beth

Tom

1 Tina's wearing **slippers** / **flip flops** / **sneakers**.

2 She's wearing a **sweater** / **sweat suit** and a **shirt** / **dress**.

3 Beth's wearing a **jacket** / **robe**.

4 She's wearing **shoes** / **slippers**.

5 Tom's wearing a **T-shirt** / **sweater**.

6 He's wearing a **scarf** / **cap**.

4 🎧 02 📋 Listen and color.

Vocabulary challenge: temperature

5 Look, choose, and write.

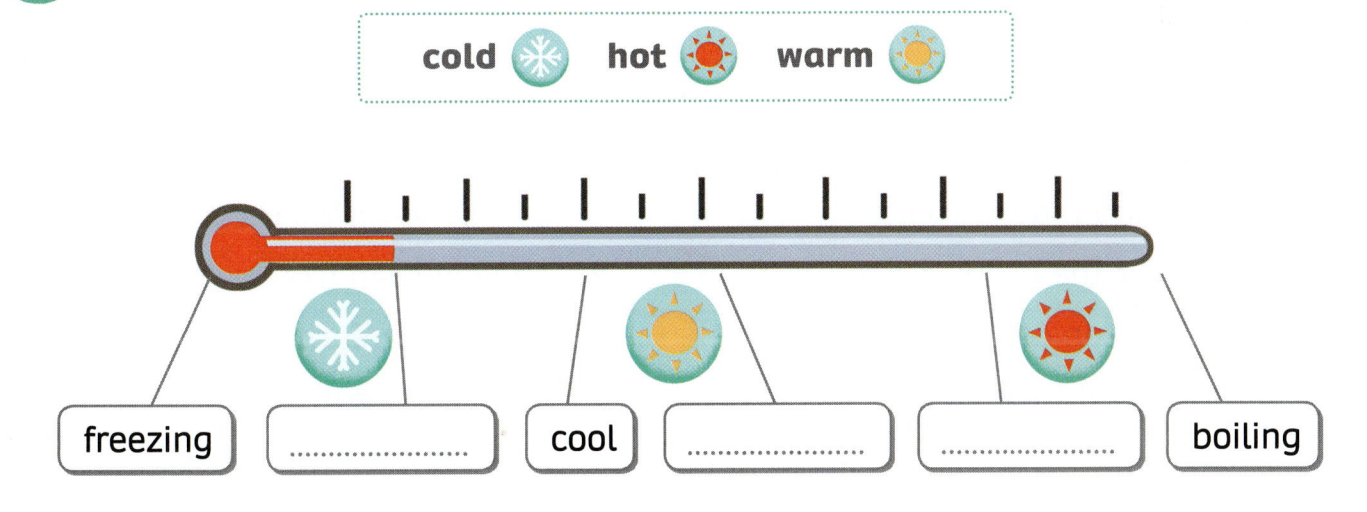

cold ❄️   hot ☀️   warm ☀️

freezing | .... | cool | .... | .... | boiling

6 Look at Activity 5. Read and write.

1 Which word means very, very hot? ....
2 Which word means very, very cold? ....
3 Which word means the weather isn't cold and isn't warm? ....

39

Reading 2

1 Read *Our Favourite Weather*. Look, read, and match.

a
b
c
d

1. The children are running. They're flying kites. ☐
2. The children are too hot. They're playing on the beach. ☐
3. The children are too cold. They're making snowmen. ☐
4. The children are wet. They're splashing in puddles. ☐

2 Read *Our Favourite Weather* again and check (✓).

1. The wind's blowing, the children are
   a wearing hats and scarves. ☐
   b too cold. ☐
   c putting on their boots. ☐
2. It's sunny, the children are
   a putting on coats and hats. ☐
   b taking off their coats. ☐
   c running. ☐
3. It's raining, the children are
   a putting up umbrellas. ☐
   b playing on the beach. ☐
   c taking off their coats. ☐
4. The children like
   a sunny weather. ☐
   b windy weather. ☐
   c all kinds of weather. ☐

3 💡 Think and write.

1. What's your favorite weather? ....
2. What are you wearing? ....
3. What are you doing? ....

Grammar 2

I**'m** runn**ing**.
You**'re** wear**ing** a robe.
He**'s** talk**ing**.
We**'re** play**ing** soccer.
You**'re** wear**ing** caps.
They**'re** putt**ing** up their umbrellas.

1 Look, read, and circle.

¹ **It's** / **You're** wearing nice sunglasses, Mia!

It's raining. ² **It's** / **We're** wearing boots, but ³ **they're** / **it's** wearing flip flops!

⁴ **You're** / **I'm** wearing my new sneakers. This is my dad. ⁵ **It's** / **He's** wearing a sweater. This is my mom. ⁶ **She's** / **We're** wearing a scarf. This is my dog. ⁷ **It's** / **They're** wearing a cap!

2 Read and write.

1 Look at my new T-shirt!
   _I'm_ wearing a new T-shirt.
2 My sister's watching a movie.
   _____ watching a movie.
3 The monkey's playing tennis!
   _____ playing tennis!
4 My friend and I are wearing jeans.
   _____ wearing jeans.

5 My dad's putting on brown shoes.
   _____ putting on brown shoes.
6 The children are wearing flip flops.
   _____ wearing flip flops.
7 I like your sneakers.
   _____ wearing sneakers.

3 Write sentences. Then look and match.

1 She / wear / sneakers.
She's wearing sneakers.

2 They / wear / jeans.

3 He / wear / flip flops.

☺ I **love** my scarf.   ☹ I **hate** my sweat suit.

4 What about you? Read and circle.

1 I **love** / **hate** my cap. It's too big, and I can't see!
2 I **love** / **hate** my sweater. It's too hot.
3 I **love** / **hate** my red T-shirt. Red's my favorite color.

5 Draw and write about your clothes.

I love my _____ .   I hate my _____ .

Writing

1 Look, choose, and write.

Remember
1 Read.
2 Get ready to write.
3 Now write!

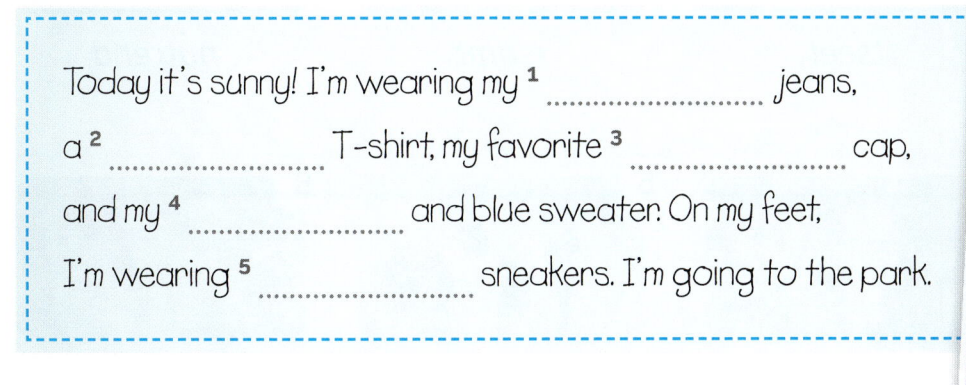

| black   blue   brown   gray   white |

Today it's sunny! I'm wearing my ¹ .... jeans, a ² .... T-shirt, my favorite ³ .... cap, and my ⁴ .... and blue sweater. On my feet, I'm wearing ⁵ .... sneakers. I'm going to the park.

2 Write for you.

1 What day is it? ....
2 What's the weather like today? ....
3 What are you wearing? ....
4 What are you doing? ....

3 Draw a picture of your clothes and write a journal. Use the sentences in Activity 2.

43

Now I Know

1 Look and write the letters in order.

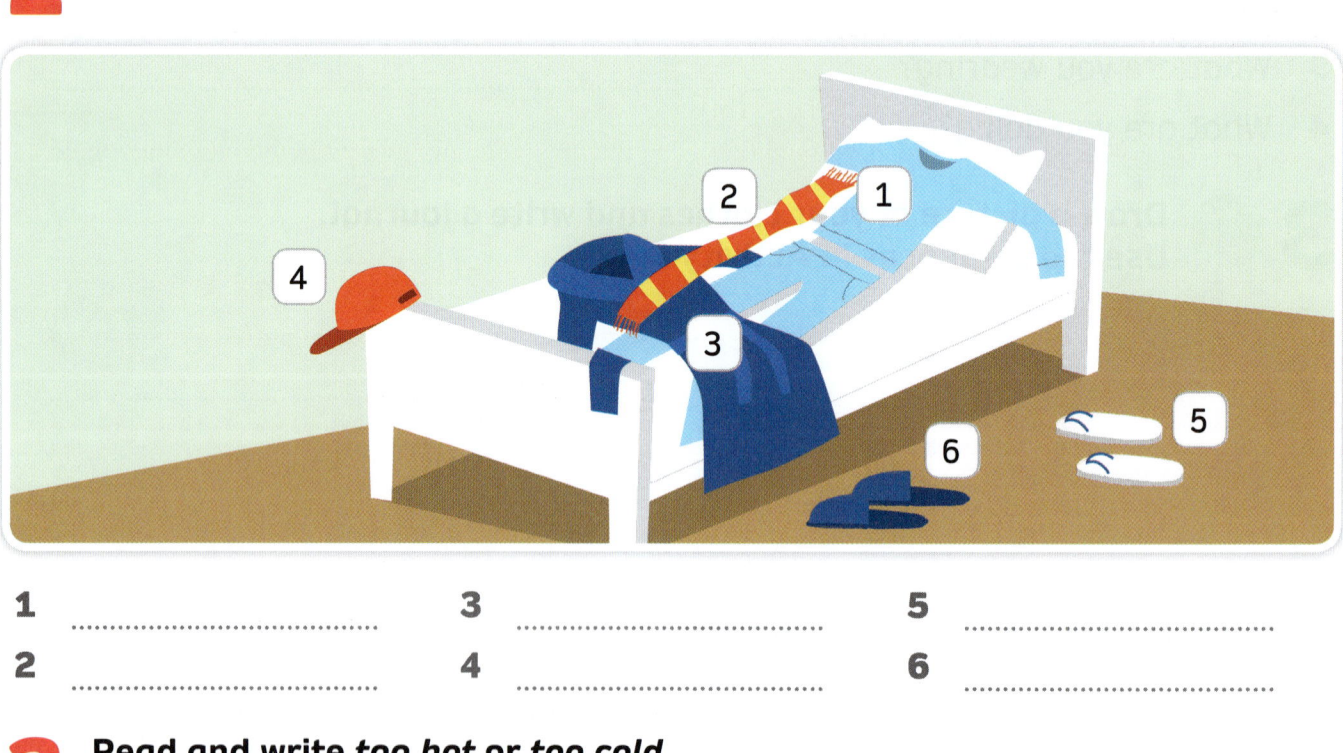

1. ygogf
2. higlngtni
3. tseel
4. ihla
5. rsomt
6. iydwn
7. nutrehd
8. atrdoon

2 Look and write.

1 .... 3 .... 5 ....
2 .... 4 .... 6 ....

3 Read and write *too hot* or *too cold*.

1 I'm not wearing a scarf today. It's .... !
2 I'm not wearing flip flops today. It's .... !

44

4 Look and write. Use color words.

1 What's she wearing?
   She ....
   ....

2 What's he wearing?
   He ....
   ....

Things I learn

1 What weather words do you know?
     What clothes are you wearing in that weather?

It's *windy* .... I'm wearing *a sweat suit* ....
It's .... I'm wearing ....

2 My new words! Draw and write.

| .... | .... | .... |

3 My favorite words in this unit!

My three favorite words in this unit are ....

4 What can you find in big cities?

What do you know?

1 What do you learn about in this unit? Read and complete.

We learn the names of places in and around our ....

2 Watch the video. Number the sentences in the correct order.

.... They put the glue on the paper.   .... They stick the boxes together.
.... They cut the paper.   .... They put the paper on the boxes.
.... They put the paint on the paper.

3 Watch the video again. Circle **T** (true) or **F** (false).

1 The library isn't very big.   T   F
2 In the town, there's a library and a sweet shop.   T   F
3 They're closing the door of the sweet shop.   T   F
4 There's a playground in the town.   T   F
5 Miranda is at the sweet shop.   T   F

4 Draw yourself in your favorite place in your town/city and write. What are you doing?

My favorite place in my town/city is the ....
I'm ....

Vocabulary 1

1 🎧 03 📋 Listen and check (✓).

1 Where's Jack?

a ☐   b ☐   c ☐

2 Where are Martina and her dad?

a ☐   b ☐   c ☐

3 Where are the children going?

a ☐   b ☐   c ☐

2 Find and circle five words for places.
Use the extra letters to write another word.

mobookstorevilibraryeplaygroundtherestaurantatbanker

1 .... 3 .... 5 ....
2 .... 4 .... 6 ....

47

3 Read, choose, and write.

> bank   bookstore   computer store   library   movie theater
> playground   restaurant   toy store

THINGS TO DO TODAY!

- Go to the ¹ .... and get money for shopping.
- Buy a new laptop bag from the ² ....
- Buy Maria a new doll at the ³ ....
- Go to the ⁴ .... and eat pizza for lunch!
- Go to the ⁵ .... to buy Dad a new book.
- Take books back to the ⁶ ....
- Play at the ⁷ .... !
- Tonight: buy tickets for the ⁸ .... !

Word study: compound words

4 Read, then look and write.

Some words for places have two parts: play + ground = playground

1 movie + ... = ...

2 .... + ... = ...

48

Reading 1

1 Read *Open and Closed*. Check (✓) the places Bobby, Tommy, and his mom go to. Then write the places in the correct order.

bookstore ☐   toy store ☐   bank ☐
library ☐   candy store ☐   movie theater ☐
computer store ☐   playground ☐
grocery store ✓   restaurant ☐

grocery store ....

....

2 Read *Open and Closed* again and write.

1 How old is Tommy? ....
2 How old is his cousin? ....
3 What does Bobby want? ....
4 Is Bobby happy or angry at the candy store? ....
5 Is the library open? ....
6 Is Bobby happy or angry in the library? ....

3 What's true for you? Read and circle.

1 It's 11 o'clock at night. Your school is **open** / **closed**.
2 It's 10:30 in the morning on Thursday. The library is **open** / **closed**.
3 It's Saturday afternoon. The playground is **open** / **closed**.

4 Draw the hands on the clock. Read and write.

It's .... The .... in my **town** / **city** is ....

49

Grammar 1

I'm **not** sleeping!
You **aren't** sleeping.
She **is not** sleeping.
She **isn't** sleeping.

1 Look, read, and circle.

1 **It's / It isn't** raining. People **are / aren't** shopping.

2 **It's / It isn't** sunny.
People **are / aren't** getting wet.

3 The bus **is / isn't** stopping.
The woman **is / isn't** shouting.

4 The woman **is / isn't** opening an umbrella.

5 We **are / aren't** getting wet.

2 Look at Picture 1 below and circle **T** (true) or **F** (false).

1	The sun isn't shining.	T	F
2	The children aren't digging.	T	F
3	Sam isn't reading.	T	F
4	The cat isn't sleeping	T	F
5	Mom isn't watching TV.	T	F

3 Look at Picture 2 in Activity 2 and write five differences.

1 The sun _isn't shining_. The wind _is blowing_. (shine / blow)
2 The two children _____.
   They _____ next to the hole. (dig / stand)
3 Sam _____. He _____. (draw / read)
4 The cat _____. It _____ water. (sleep / drink)
5 Mom _____. She _____ the window. (cook / clean)

Vocabulary 2

1 Read and circle.

1. The **train / car** is at the gas station.
2. You can buy fruits and vegetables at the **factory / market**.
3. You can buy a train ticket at the **gas station / train station**.
4. They make cars and machines at the **market / factory**.
5. There are sheep and cows in the **small town / fields**.
6. Our house is on **traffic / a street**.
7. There are many streets in a **small town / field**.
8. Beep, Beep! There **is so much traffic / are so many markets** in the street!

2 Look, choose, and write. Then complete the sentences.

factory   gas station   market
playground   street   train station

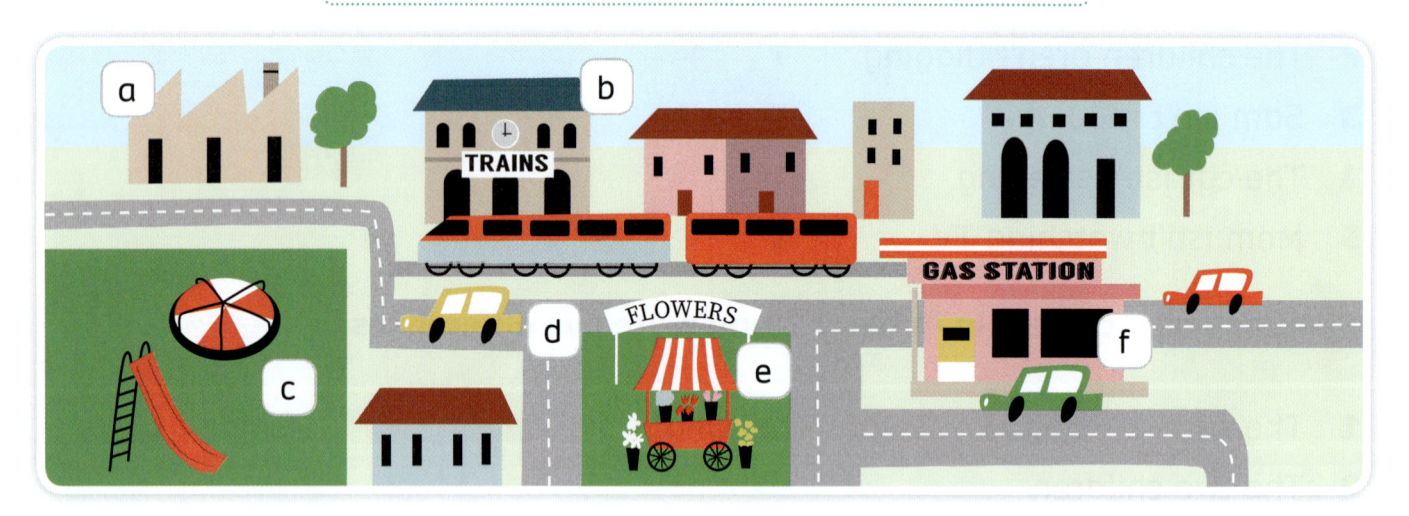

a ....   c ....   e ....
b ....   d ....   f ....

1. Is this a city or a small town? It's a ....
2. Is there a lot of traffic? ....
3. There's a .... at the train station.
4. There's a .... at the gas station.
5. You can buy .... at the market.

52

3 Read and match.

1 We need gas for our car.
2 Our train leaves at one o'clock.
3 We need fruits and vegetables.
4 There's a lot of traffic.
5 I want to play soccer and fly a kite.

a This street is very noisy.
b Let's go to the market.
c Let's go to the gas station.
d Let's go to the fields.
e Let's go to the train station.

Vocabulary challenge: city words

4 Look, choose, and write.

bus stop   corner   crosswalk
parking lot   sidewalk   traffic light

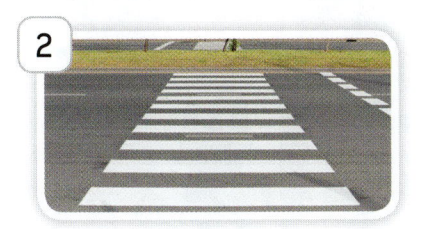

1 ....
2 ....
3 ....
4 ....
5 ....
6 ....

5 Read and circle.

1 When you want to travel by bus, wait at the **parking lot** / **bus stop**.
2 There are a lot of cars **on the sidewalk** / **in the parking lot**.
3 Walk on the **traffic light** / **sidewalk**.
4 The bank's at the **corner** / **crosswalk** of the street.
5 Stop when the **corner** / **traffic light** is red.
6 Do you want to walk across the street? Use the **crosswalk** / **parking lot**.

53

Reading 2

1 Read *Where I Live* and circle.

1 Anna **knows / doesn't know** everyone in the town.
2 There **are / aren't** a lot of children in Anna's school.
3 There are a lot of stores in the small **town / city**.
4 Anna and her friends play in the **factory / fields**.
5 Scott **goes / doesn't go** to the movie theater.
6 The streets in Scott's neighborhood are **busy / quiet**.

2 Read *Where I Live* again. Choose and write.

> candy store   library   mall
> playground   traffic

1 There's a _____ and a lot of grocery stores in Scott's neighborhood.
2 Across the street from Anna's school, there's a _____ .
3 Scott likes the movie theater and the _____ .
4 The street in front of Scott's school has a lot of _____ .
5 Scott plays with his friends on the _____ .

3 Think and write.

1 Is your school big or small?
2 What stores are in your neighborhood?
3 What do you like about where you live?
4 What don't you like?

Grammar 2

behind   in front of   between   across from

1 Look, read, and write. Use *behind*, *in front of*, *between*, and *across from*.

1 The stores are ………………… the school.
2 The children are playing ………………… the school.
3 The bus is ………………… the car.
4 The library is ………………… the grocery store and the bookstore.

2 Draw a street in a town/city and write. Where are the buildings?

> **Are** they play**ing** a game?
> **Yes** they **are**.
>
> **Are** they play**ing** tennis?
> **No**, they **aren't**.
>
> **Is** he hid**ing** behind the tree?
> **Yes**, he **is**.
>
> **Is** he hid**ing** in front of the tree?
> **No**, he **isn't**.

3 Read and circle.

1 **Is** / **Are** Joe running? Yes, he **is** / **are**.
2 **Am** / **Are** you having lunch? No, I **isn't** / **'m not**.
3 **Is** / **Are** you and your friends shopping? Yes, we **is** / **are**.

4 Look and write the words in order to make questions.

1 Kate / sit / the tree / in front of

Is Kate sitting in front of the tree ?

2 run / the field / Jim / across from

.... ?

3 run / behind / Mom / the house

.... ?

4 eat / the goats / the flowers

.... ?

5 Look at Activity 4. Write the answers.

1 *Yes, she is.*
2 ....
3 ....
4 ....

56

Writing

1 Read and write. Use *There is* or *There are*.

Remember
1. Read.
2. Get ready to write.
3. Now write!

I live in a small town. It's called Newfields. It isn't very big, but ¹ _there are_ a lot of stores. ² _____ a train station. ³ _____ two gas stations. ⁴ _____ a big park between my school and the library. The library's my favorite place. ⁵ _____ a lot of books, computers, and games. ⁶ _____ a playground behind the library. Here's a picture of me and my friends. We're running and jumping at the playground!

2 Check (✓) the places in your town or city.

bookstore ☐   candy store ☐   factory ☐   gas station ☐
library ☐   park ☐   playground ☐   train station ☐

3 Draw and write about your town or city. Use *There is/are* and the words in the box.

across from   behind
between   in front of

My town/city is called _____.
There is _____
_____
_____
_____

57

Now I Know

1 Look, read, and circle. Then choose and write.

bank   candy store   factory   library   market   school

There ¹ **is** / **are** two stores on King Street. There ² **is** / **are** a bookstore between the restaurant and the toy store. Across from the restaurant there ³ **is** / **are** a ⁴ .... The children are playing on the playground ⁵ **in front of** / **behind** the school. There ⁶ **is** / **are** a ⁷ .... on King Street, too. It's between the school and the bank. There ⁸ **is** / **are** a movie theater in the town. It's on Queen Street, behind the ⁹ .... There are two other places on Queen Street: a ¹⁰ .... and a gas station. Across from the candy store there is a ¹¹ .... It's next to the train station. Across from the movie theater, there is a big park with trees and grass. Today there is a ¹² .... there.

58

2 Read and circle.

1 He **isn't standing** / **standing** in front of the library.
2 You **'re hide** / **'re hiding** behind a tree.
3 They **aren't running** / **don't runs** across from the street.
4 I **'m sit** / **'m sitting** between a box and a ball.

3 Read and write.

1 _Is_ the man _cleaning_ (clean) the toy store window?
2 _____ the children _____ (buy) candy?
3 _____ it _____ (rain)?
4 _____ the children _____ (play) soccer?

Things I learn

1 What can you find in your town/city? Write six places.

There is _____ .
There are _____ .

2 My new words! Draw and write.

3 My favorite words in this unit!

My three favorite words in this unit are _____ .

5 How do we celebrate?

What do you know?

1 What do you learn about in this unit? Read and complete.

We learn words to talk about celebrating a b_____ p_____ .

2 🎬 BBC Watch the video. Read, choose, and write.

> eighteen   fifteen   five   six   three

1 There are _____ people at Bill's birthday party.
2 Bill and his friends want _____ cakes.
3 There are _____ mangoes in each milkshake.
4 Sally needs _____ mangoes to make the milkshakes.
5 Sally makes _____ milkshakes.

3 🎬 BBC Watch the video again. Read and circle.

1 There are ten **mangoes** / **people** at the party.
2 Mom has ten pieces of **watermelon** / **mango**.
3 **Three** / **Two** people say, "No, thanks".
4 **Two** / **Eight** pieces of watermelon are left.

4 Circle which food and drinks you want to have at your birthday party. Write one more example of each.

Food: cakes   mangoes   watermelon   _____
Drinks: water   fruit juice   cans of soda   _____

Vocabulary 1

1 🎧 04 📋 **Listen and draw lines.**

2 **Read and write the letters in order.**

1. Eat some fruit *ladsa* _____. There's lots of fruit in it!
2. Pour the *shamkekil* _____ into the glass. Mmm, it's delicious.
3. How many *decalns* _____ are there on your birthday cake?
4. Are you hungry? Have a *kacepuc* _____.
5. I love eating sweet *copnorp* _____.
6. Can I have a *rugber* _____ with cheese and fries?
7. We all write our names in our teacher's birthday *crad* _____.
8. Oh, look! The wind is blowing a big, red *lolabno* _____ away!

61

3 Read and write. Then color.

It's my birthday! I'm having a party! There are a lot of ¹ .... There's a ² .... card from my mom and dad on the table. Dad's cooking ³ .... for us to eat! I have a birthday cake with nine ⁴ .... on it. I'm making strawberry ⁵ .... to drink. To eat, there are delicious chocolate ⁶ .... and ⁷ ...., and some ⁸ .... with oranges, bananas, and strawberries. Mmm!

Word study: -s with words we can count

4 Look at the words. Circle the letter that's different. Then complete the rule.

1 cake – cakes   2 apple – apples   3 candle – candles   4 egg – eggs

We write .... at the end of words we can count.

5 Check (✓) the things you can count. Cross (✗) the things you can't count.

1 cupcake ☐   4 rice ☐   7 burger ☐
2 popcorn ☐   5 water ☐   8 tea ☐
3 balloon ☐   6 card ☐   9 milkshake ☐

6 Look at Activity 5. Write the words we can count. Add one more example.

1 ....   3 ....   5 ....
2 ....   4 ....   6 ....

Reading 1

1 Read *Surprise!* and match.

1. Lucy asks her friends
2. Her friends can't come because
3. At home, Lucy is sad because
4. Lucy goes to the stores because
5. Lucy is happy because

a. all her friends are at the party.
b. they have after school clubs.
c. they need milk for the milkshakes.
d. to come to her party.
e. she has no friends.

2 Read *Surprise!* again and write.

1. What time is Lucy's party?
　...
2. Who's helping Lucy with the food and decorations?
　...
3. What is there to eat and drink at the party?
　...
4. What do Lucy's friends bring to the party?
　...

3 💡 Think of a gift for your mom, your dad, and your best friend. Draw and write.

This is a gift for my mom.
It's ....

This is a gift for my dad.
It's ....

This is a gift for my friend.
It's ....

Grammar 1

> I have **some** juice. I don't have **any** milk.

1 Read and circle.

Adam: It's Larry's birthday soon. Let's buy him a gift. What about a game or a puzzle?

Tina: He has ¹ **some** / **any** video games, but he doesn't have ² **some** / **any** puzzles.

Adam: What else does he like? He loves trains.

Sales clerk: Look, we have ³ **some** / **any** great toy trains! Does he like reading, too?

Adam: Yes, he does.

Sales clerk: We also have ⁴ **some** / **any** books about trains.

Adam: Larry doesn't have ⁵ **some** / **any** books about trains.

Tina: That's true. Let's buy him one.

Sales clerk: How about this book? It's very popular.

Adam: That looks great! There's only one problem. I don't have ⁶ **some** / **any** money!

2 Read and write *some* or *any*.

1 They have _____ paper.
2 They don't have _____ crayons.
3 They have _____ pictures.
4 They have _____ scissors.
5 They don't have _____ glue.
6 They don't have _____ gold stars, but they have _____ silver stars.

3 Preeti and Diego are having their birthday parties. What do they/don't they have? Find and write six more differences. Use *some* and *any*.

Preeti doesn't have any fruit salad.
Diego has some balloons.

4 Choose and write sentences. What do/don't you have in your kitchen?

| bananas | birthday cake | chocolate | coconuts |
| eggs | fruit | milk | milkshakes | tea |

We don't have any coconuts.

Vocabulary 2

1 Read and circle.

1 You can swim here. — swimming pool / ice rink
2 You can climb, run, jump, and play. — aquarium / adventure playground
3 You can skate here. — ice rink / theme park
4 You can watch birds here. — nature center / arts center
5 You can see fish here – and jellyfish! — swimming pool / aquarium
6 You can go bowling here. — theme park / bowling alley
7 You can draw and paint here. — arts center / nature center
8 You can play in castles here. — ice rink / theme park

2 Where are the children having their birthday parties? Look and write.

3 What's your favorite place for a party? What can you do there? Draw and write.

My favorite place for a party is the _____.
You can _____ there.

Vocabulary challenge: action words

4 Read and match. Then look and number.

1 surprise   a make something pretty
2 invite   b put things in place
3 decorate   c ask a friend to come to a party
4 prepare   d do something in secret

5 Read and write. Use the words from Activity 4.

I want to ¹ _____ my friends to my birthday party on Saturday. I want to ² _____ my room with balloons. My brother wants to help me ³ _____ the table. There will be cupcakes, candles, orange juice, and popcorn. I want to ⁴ _____ my friends – we can go to an adventure playground first, then come home to eat.

67

Reading 2

1 Read *Amazing Parties* and check (✓).

	CUPCAKE PARTY	PIRATE PARTY	SAFARI PARTY	POOL PARTY
1 You can decorate your food with flowers.				
2 You can wear animal masks.				
3 You can play on a ship.				
4 You can swim.				
5 You can make jungle decorations.				

2 Read *Amazing Parties* again and match.

1 You can have a cupcake party   a at a pirate party.
2 You can have a safari party   b at a theme park.
3 You can have a pirate party   c at a bowling alley or ice rink.
4 You can't eat cake   d at an arts center or nature center.
5 You can make hats and flags   e in the swimmming pool.

3 Draw and complete your party invitation.

To ....
From ....
My party is on .... day.
It's at .... o'clock.

68

Grammar 2

Would you **like** some juice?   Yes, please. / No, thanks.
Can I **have** some juice, please?   Here you go!

1 Read and circle.

1. Would you like some bananas? / Can I have some bananas, please?
   — Here you go!

2. Would you like some water? / Can I have some water, please?
   — Yes, please.

3. Would you like some ice cream? / Can I have some ice cream, please?
   — No, thanks.

4. Would you like some fruit salad? / Can I have some fruit salad, please?
   — Here you go!

2 Read, choose, and write.

> Here you go!   Here you go!   No, thanks.
> No, thanks.   ~~Yes, please.~~

1. Would you like to go to a party? (✓) _Yes, please._
2. Can I have some burgers, please? (✓) _____
3. Would you like a glass of milk? (✗) _____
4. Can I have some fruit salad, please? (✓) _____
5. Would you like to watch a DVD? (✗) _____

3 Write the words in order to make questions.

1 you / like / Would / soda / some

   ....?

2 I / some / please / have / Can / cookies

   ....?

3 you / to the park / Would / to go / like

   ....?

4 have / I / some / Can / please / cake

   ....?

5 to paint / face / your / you / Would / like

   ....?

4 Look at the example. Write questions and answers.

1 **Katy:** go skating? — Would you like to go skating?
   Tom: ✓ — Yes, please.

2 **Raheem:** some juice? — Would you like some juice?
   Anna: ✗ — No, thanks.

3 **Nina:** some tea?
   Aishe: ✓

4 **Tom:** some bread?
   Mat: ✗

5 **Nick:** go swimming?
   Sara: ✓

Writing

Remember
1 Read.
2 Get ready to write.
3 Now write!

1 Read, choose, and write the letter.

a   We have some milkshakes, too.
b   we have party hats, too.
c   My mom and dad are there, too.
d   they give me cards, too.

It's my birthday party. My friends are there. ¹ __c__
We're having a party in the yard. We have balloons and
² .... I have a chocolate cake. It has decorations on it.
We have fruit salad, cookies, and ice cream. ³ ....
My friends give me gifts and ⁴ ....

2 Read and write.

I'm going to send invitations to:
.... , ... , ...

We can have these decorations:
.... ,
.... ,
....

We need this food and drink:
.... ,
.... ,
....

My Birthday Party

We can play these games / do these things:
.... , ... , ...

3 Draw and write about your birthday party.

I'm having a birthday party! I'm .... years old today.
My friends ....
....
....
....

71

Now I Know

1 Find and color six party things. Then write.

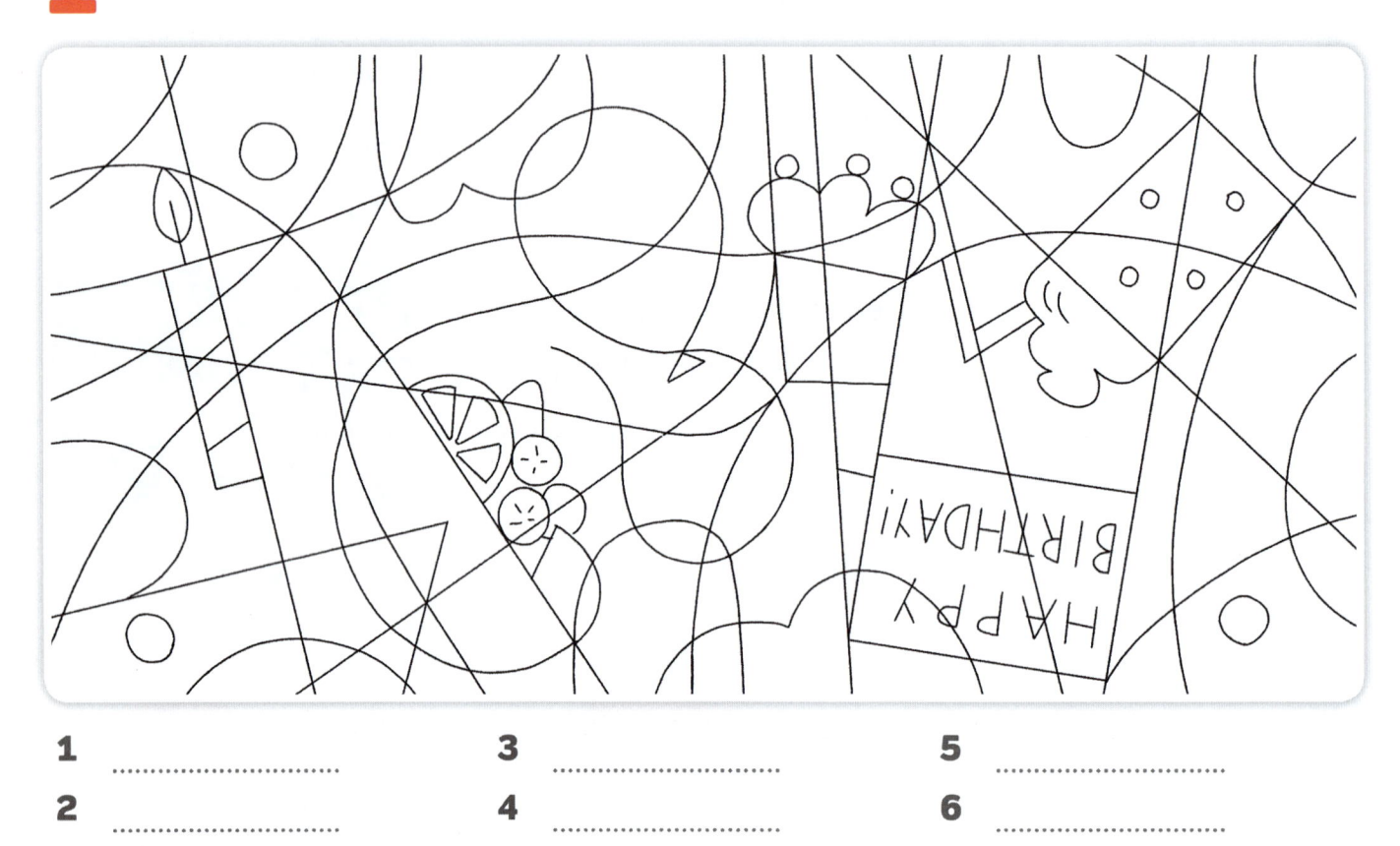

1 .... 3 .... 5 ....
2 .... 4 .... 6 ....

2 Read, choose, and write.

> adventure playground   aquarium   arts center
> bowling alley   ice rink   nature center
> swimming pool   theme park

1 We can go bowling at the ....
2 We can skate at the ....
3 We can play on a pirate ship at the ....
4 We can see birds, butterflies, and animals at the ....
5 We can paint, draw, and make masks at the ....
6 We can swim in the ....
7 We can see different kinds of fish at the ....
8 We can climb, run, and jump at the ....

3 Read, choose, and write.

> Can I have   Here you go!   No, thanks.   Would you like
> Would you like   Yes, please.

Mom: 1 .... a milkshake, Billie?
Billie: 2 .... I love milkshakes!
Mom: 3 .... some fruit salad?
Billie: 4 .... I don't like fruit salad. But I love ice cream!
       5 .... some ice cream, please?
Mom: 6 ....

Things I learn

1 Where can you celebrate your birthday? Write six places.

....
....

2 My new words! Draw and write.

3 My favorite words in this unit!

My three favorite words in this unit are ....

6 What jobs can I do?

What do you know?

1 What do you learn about in this unit? Read and complete.

We learn about .... we can do.

2 Watch the video. Number the jobs they mime in the correct order.

.... cleaner   .... policeman
.... teacher   .... pilot
.... mechanic

3 Watch the video again. Read and circle.

1 **Kitty** / **Max** doesn't know how to mime.
2 **Kitty** / **Max** mimes a job first.
3 You **can** / **can't** speak when you're miming.
4 You **can** / **can't** use your hands when you're miming.
5 Kitty is flying a **real** / **paper** plane.

4 Write three things you like doing. What do you want to be one day? Draw.

I like ....,
................................, and
....
I want to be a ....

Vocabulary 1

1 Read and circle.

1. This food is delicious. You're a good **astronaut / chef**!
2. My dog is sick. Take it to the **doctor / vet**.
3. That man is a thief! Call the **police officer / hairdresser**!
4. My knee hurts. Go to the **dentist / doctor**.
5. Is there water on the moon? I don't know. Ask **a police officer / an astronaut**.
6. Your hair is too long. Go to the **chef / hairdresser**.
7. If your tooth hurts, go to the **dentist / vet**.
8. Are you a **hairdresser / photographer**? Can you take my picture, please?

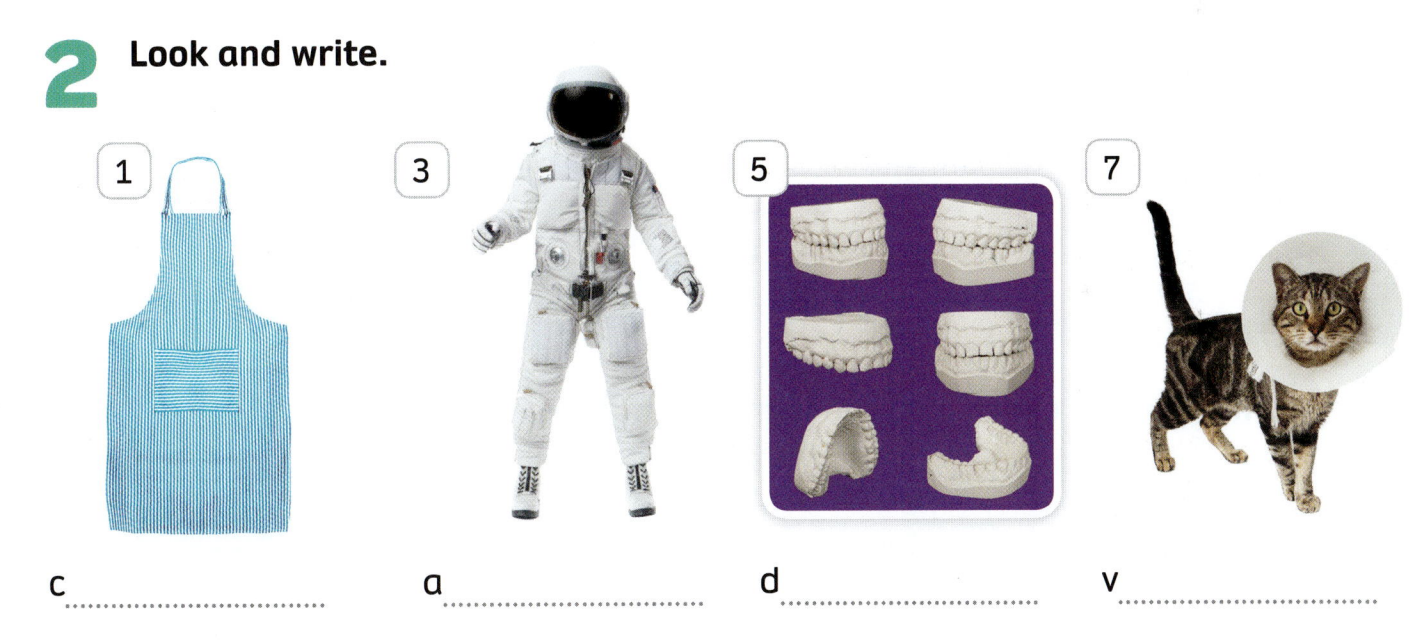

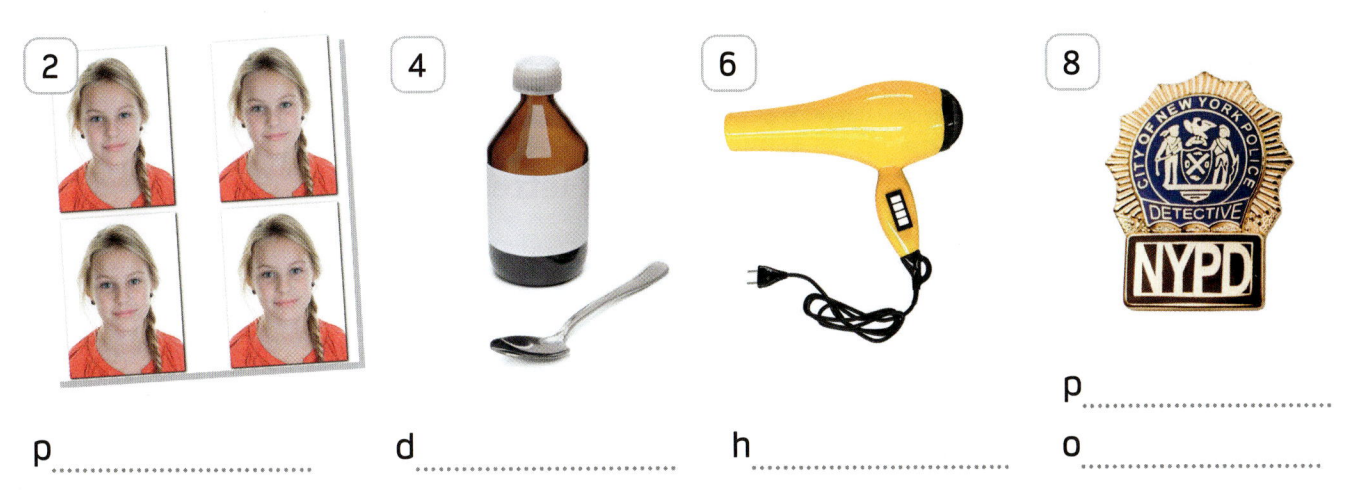

2 Look and write.

1. c_____
2. p_____
3. a_____
4. d_____
5. d_____
6. h_____
7. v_____
8. p_____
   o_____

75

3 Read and write.

1 A .... cuts my hair.
2 An .... travels to the moon.
3 A .... works in a hospital.
4 A .... takes pictures.
5 A .... helps animals.
6 A .... cooks food.
7 A .... looks at teeth.
8 A .... drives a police car.

Word study: -er, -or, and -ist

4 Add -er, -or, or -ist.

1 photograph........
2 hairdress........
3 dent........
4 doct........
5 sail........
6 art........
7 act........
8 teach........
9 journal........

5 Complete the chart. Use the words from Activity 4.

-er	-or	-ist
photographer		

6 What jobs do your parents do? What letters do their job words end with?

....
....

Reading 1

1 Read *Sam's Job* and circle **T** (true) or **F** (false).

1 It's Sam's birthday tomorrow.   T   F
2 Sam is good at cooking.   T   F
3 Sam is too young to be a police officer.   T   F
4 Sam is good at running.   T   F
5 Sam takes Mr. Clark's dog for a walk.   T   F
6 Sam gives his mom 30 dollars.   T   F

2 Read *Sam's Job* again and match.

1 Sam is   a a spaceship.
2 Sam isn't   b eight.
3 Sam can't   c dogs.
4 Sam likes   d be a doctor or a vet.
5 Sam buys   e good at cooking.
6 Sam doesn't have f three books.

3 Ask your friend what he/she is and isn't good at. Then write and draw a job for them.

1 What are you good at?

....

....

2 What aren't you good at?

....

....

3 You can be a ....

77

Grammar 1

> I **want** to be a soccer player!   I **don't want** to be a pilot.
> She **wants** to be an astronaut.   She **doesn't want** to be a chef.
> **Do** you **want** to be a vet? **Yes**, I **do**. / **No**, I **don't**.

1 Read and circle.

1 I like flying in a plane. I want to be a **pilot** / **teacher**.
2 I like taking dogs for a walk. I want to be **a dog walker** / **an astronaut**.
3 I like cleaning. I want to be a **hairdresser** / **cleaner**.
4 I like dancing. I want to be a **nurse** / **dancer**.

2 Look, read, and write.

1 I ….want…. to be a police officer.

3 I want …………… a nurse.

5 I …………… a clown.

2 I want …………… be an artist.

4 I …………… an astronaut.

6 …………… a scientist.

78

3 Read and write *want(s) to* or *don't/doesn't want to*.

1 I _____ eat a burger. (✓)
2 She _____ be a soccer player. (✗)
3 I _____ be a vet. (✗)
4 He _____ be a police officer. (✓)
5 I _____ be a hairdresser. (✗)

4 Write for you.

1 Do you want to be an astronaut? _____
2 Do you like to help people? _____
3 Do you want to be a chef? _____
4 Do you like animals? _____
5 Do you like to speak English? _____

5 Use words from both boxes to write sentences.

a | to buy   to clean   to go   to read   to take |

b | a gift for my friend   a picture of you   a story   the house   to the park |

1 I want _____ .
2 I don't want _____ .
3 She _____ .
4 He _____ .
5 _____ .

6 What about you? Read and write *want* or *don't want*.

1 I _____ to be a scientist.
2 I _____ to be an artist.
3 I _____ to be a teacher.
4 I _____ to be police officer.

79

Vocabulary 2

1 Read and circle.

1 **Sofia:** How do you call your dog?
  Leo: I **perform** / **whistle**!

2 **Alex:** Do you **whistle** / **study** math?
  Val: Yes, and science, too.

3 **Mia:** Are you a mechanic?
  Lucas: Yes, I can **cook** / **fix** your car.

4 **Ava:** Are you doing your homework?
  Noah: Yes. **Check** / **Clean** my answers, please.

5 **Clara:** This box is very big!
  Tom: I can **fix** / **help** you with it.

6 **Yve:** Why are they singing?
  Oli: They're **performing** / **checking** in the school show.

7 **Harry:** The windows are dirty.
  Mat: Let's **help** / **clean** them.

8 **Mia:** Is your dad a chef?
  Sam: Yes. He **cleans** / **cooks** delicious food.

2 Look and write the letters in order.

1 w e s i h l t

2 i x f

3 e l n a c

4 o k c o

5 r p o m f r e

3 Read, choose, and write.

> check   clean   help   perform   study

I'm a teacher. Every day is a busy day for me! The children in my class ¹_____ for a spelling test. They write their words, then I ²_____ their answers. In drama class, we ³_____ a play. After school, I ⁴_____ the classroom. The children ⁵_____ me. I love my job!

Vocabulary challenge: actions

4 Look, choose, and write.

> create   discover   explore   rescue

1 _____   2 _____   3 _____   4 _____

5 Read and write. Use the words from Activity 4.

1 I want to sail a boat and _____ the oceans.
2 My brother wants to be a scientist and _____ new things.
3 My best friend wants to _____ animals in trouble.
4 We like art a lot. We want to _____ cool works of art.

6 Think and write.

1 Would you like to explore the ocean? _____
2 What do scientists discover? _____

81

Reading 2

1 Read *How Can I Be an Astronaut?* and circle.

1. Astronauts **study** / **don't study** a lot.
2. There **are** / **aren't** cleaners in a spaceship.
3. It **is** / **isn't** important for astronauts to check things many times.
4. Astronauts can't **walk** / **float** in a spaceship.
5. Astronauts **take** / **don't take** pictures in space.
6. It's **fun** / **boring** in a spaceship.

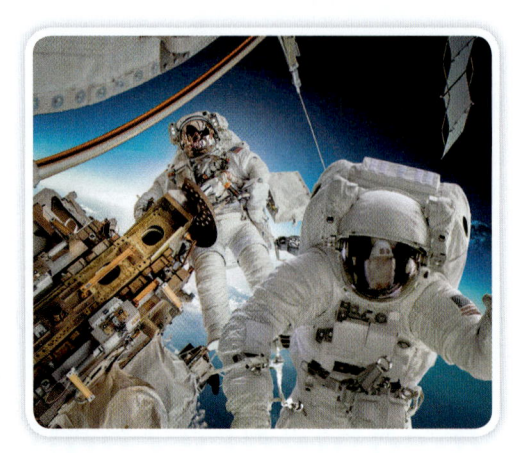

2 Read *How Can I Be an Astronaut?* again and write.

1. What do astronauts study?
   ....
2. Is it difficult to cook in the spaceship?
   ....
3. What do astronauts check in the spaceship?
   ....
4. What do astronauts take pictures of?
   ....
5. Do astronauts perform in the spaceship? What do they do?
   ....

3 You're an astronaut. What do you do in the spaceship every day? Circle one activity and draw.

I clean.   I fix equipment.
I talk to other astronauts.
I take pictures.   I float!

82

Grammar 2

♥ I **love** rid**ing** my bike!   ☹ I **don't like** perform**ing**.
☺ He **likes** swimm**ing**.   😠 I **hate** clean**ing** my bedroom.

1 Read and circle.

1 I **love / like / don't like / hate** swimming. ☺
2 I **love / like / don't like / hate** reading. ♥
3 I **love / like / don't like / hate** climbing trees. ☹
4 I **love / like / don't like / hate** watching baseball on TV. ♥
5 I **love / like / don't like / hate** fixing my bike. ☹
6 I **love / like / don't like / hate** going to the dentist. 😠

2 What about you? Read and write. Use *love*, *like*, *don't like*, or *hate*.

1 I .... taking pictures.
2 I .... singing and dancing.
3 I .... cleaning my room.
4 I .... riding a horse.
5 I .... doing science experiments.
6 I .... drawing pictures.

3 Write the words in order.

1 I / helping / animals / like
   ....
2 like / swimming / I / don't
   ....
3 cooking / like / I
   ....
4 love / people / I / making / laugh
   ....
5 fixing / cars / I / like
   ....
6 my / teeth / I / brushing / hate
   ....

4 Complete the quiz. What do you want to be?

WHAT'S A GOOD JOB FOR YOU?

	Love ♥	Like 🙂	Don't like 🙁	Hate 😠	Do you want to be a ...?
HELPING PEOPLE, TALKING TO PEOPLE					TEACHER, DOCTOR, DENTIST, NURSE
HELPING ANIMALS					VET, DOG WALKER
CLEANING					CLEANER
PERFORMING					SINGER, DANCER, CLOWN
FIXING CARS					MECHANIC
COOKING					CHEF
FLYING A PLANE					PILOT
DRIVING A CAR					TAXI DRIVER
DOING HAIR					HAIRDRESSER
PLAYING SPORTS					SOCCER PLAYER, P.E. TEACHER
COUNTING AND DOING MATH					MATH TEACHER, ASTRONAUT

5 💡 Look at your answers in Activity 4. Write for you.

I hate playing sports. I like talking to people. I love helping people. I want to be a nurse.

Writing

1 Read, choose, and write.

> **Remember**
> 1 Read.
> 2 Get ready to write.
> 3 Now write!

with a ball   with me
with my dog   with my three pets

Freddie and Me

Hi. My name's Sophie. I love animals! I want to be a vet. I like horses, cats, and rabbits, but my favorite animals are dogs. I love going to the park [1] _____ Freddie. We always play [2] _____. I throw the ball and Freddie catches it! In the evening, I watch TV, and Freddie sits [3] _____ in the living room. Here's a picture of me [4] _____ – Freddie, Fifi the cat, and Fabio the rabbit!

2 Complete the chart for you.

Things I love/like doing	With who or what?	Where?	When?
I love swimming	with my friends	in the pool	on Saturdays

3 What do you want to be? Write your blog.

Hi! My name's _____.
I want to be _____!
It's a good job for me because I like / love _____
_____
_____.

Now I Know

1 Look, match, and write the missing letters.

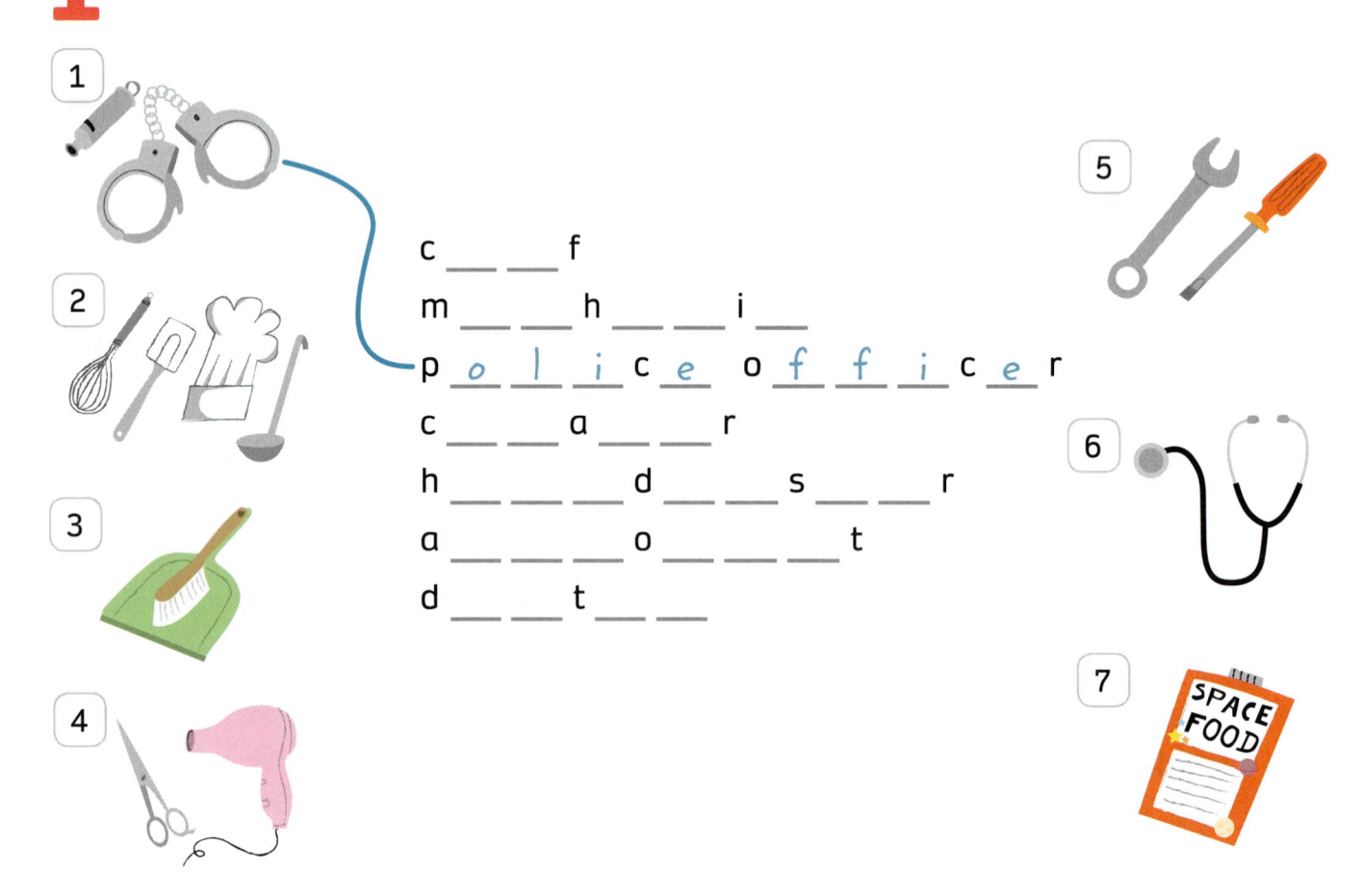

c __ __ f
m __ __ h __ __ i __
p o l i c e   o f f i c e r
c __ __ a __ __ r
h __ __ d __ __ s __ __ r
a __ __ __ o __ __ t
d __ __ t __ __

2 Look, read, and circle.

1. I want to **be** / **drive** a car!

2. I want to **buy** / **go** some ice cream, please!

3. I want to **buy** / **be** a pilot.

4. I want to **go** / **be** to the moon!

86

3 Look and write *love*, *like*, *don't like*, or *hate*.

Amy	cooking
Ben	talking with friends
Cody	cleaning
Dan	helping people
Emily	running

Amy: I don't like cooking.
Ben: ....
Cody: ....
Dan: ....
Emily: ....

Things I learn

1 Which jobs do you know? Write four jobs.

....

2 My new words! Draw and write.

3 My favorite words in this unit!

My three favorite words in this unit are ....

87

7 Why do we play sports?

What do you know?

1 What do you learn about in this unit? Read and complete.

We learn the names of different ....

2 🎬 BBC 7-1 Watch the video. Check (✓) the things you can do and cross (✗) the things you can't do.

1. kick a baseball ☐
2. run with a basketball ☐
3. take off your helmet when you ride a horse ☐
4. jump on the mat in gymnastics ☐
5. play table tennis with one, two, or three friends ☐
6. kick the other person in judo ☐

3 🎬 BBC 7-1 Read and write the sport. Watch the video again to check.

1. You can run and bounce the ball. ....
2. You can hold the reins. ....
3. You can hold the other person. ....

4 What's your favorite sport? Is it a team sport? Draw and write.

My favorite sport is ....

....

It is/isn't ....

....

Vocabulary 1

1 Write the missing letters.

1. w __ __ er __ o __ o
2. f __ __ __ d   h __ __ __ ey
3. pad __ le __ oa __ __ ing
4. b __ __ m __ __ ton
5. h __ __ __ eback __ __ ing
6. b __ __ e __ __ ll

2 Read and circle.

1. You use a ball in **field hockey** / **horseback riding**.
2. You can't **go skiing** / **play baseball** on your own.
3. **Paddleboarding** / **Horseback riding** is a water sport.
4. You can play **ping-pong** / **baseball** with only two players.
5. You **play water polo** / **go skiing** in the snow.
6. You can play **water polo** / **field hockey** in a swimming pool.

89

3 Complete the chart. Check (✓) or cross (✗).

What Sports?	🏓	🏄	🚣	⛑️	⚾	🏸	🏑
It's a water sport.							
It's a team sport.							
You use a ball.							

4 Look at Activity 3. Write about the sports.

1 Badminton is a team sport.
2
3
4
5
6

Word study: vowels

5 Underline *a*, *e*, *i*, *o*, and *u*.

1 tennis
2 judo
3 bike
4 baseball
5 karate
6 soccer
7 paddleboarding
8 horseback riding
9 skiing

6 Write the missing letters *a*, *e*, *i*, *o*, and *u*.

1 p___ng-p___ng
2 b___sk___tb___ll
3 b___dm___nt___n
4 r___nn___ng
5 f___ ___ld h___ck___y
6 w___t___r p___l___
7 j___d___
8 gymn___st___cs

Reading 1

1 Read *Thank You, Ella!* Look and write.

Ella   Alexia   Julia   Miss Bright

1 .... doesn't have her whistle.
2 .... isn't good at sports.
3 .... is good at field hockey.
4 .... can't find the field hockey ball.
5 .... is good at running.
6 .... is good at badminton and baseball.

2 Read *Thank You, Ella!* again and write.

1 Miss Bright is a ....
2 Her whistle is in the ....
3 Alexia has a field hockey .... today.
4 The field hockey ball is behind a ....
5 Ella gets a .... for helping people.

3 Think and write.

1 Do you have a medal?

....

2 Why do people get medals?

....

3 What other things can you get if you win at sports?

....

91

Grammar 1

I**'m good at** swimming.
I**'m not good at** skiing!
My best friend **is good at** ping-pong.
He/She **isn't good at** dancing.

1 Read and circle.

1 My mom **is** / **are** good at fixing things.
2 I **aren't** / **'m not** good at playing the piano.
3 You're always busy. You **aren't** / **isn't** good at doing nothing!
4 My dad **am** / **is** good at driving a car.
5 My friends **isn't** / **aren't** good at cooking.
6 We **'re** / **'s** good at helping each other.

2 Look, choose, and write.

aren't good at   'm good at   isn't good at   're good at
~~'s good at~~   is good at

1 He 's good at running.
2 She _____ playing tennis.
3 My dog _____ doing tricks.
4 They _____ singing.
5 You _____ horseback riding.
6 I _____ telling jokes.

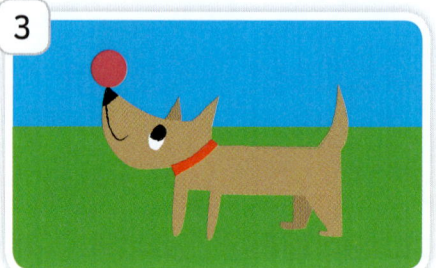

3 What are/aren't they good at? Write sentences.

1 My friend / speaking English. (✓)
   My friend is good at speaking English.

2 I / doing tricks. (✗)
   ....

3 You / winning races. (✓)
   ....

4 The children / being quiet in class. (✗)
   ....

Close your eyes.   **Count** to ten.   **Don't look**.   **Run** and **hide**.

---

4 Look, read, and write.

1 *Don't swim* here! (swim)

2 .... a helmet! (wear)

3 .... pictures! (take)

4 .... soccer here! (play)

5 Correct the school rules. Then write one more school rule.

Be late.   ~~Don't do your homework.~~   Don't listen to the teacher.

1 *Do your homework.*   3 ....
2 ....   4 ....

Vocabulary 2

1 Look, read, and circle.

1. **Throw** / **Bounce** the ball.

2. Ryan: **Catch** / **Hold** the bat in your hand.
   Dave: **Hit** / **Bounce** the ball with the bat.

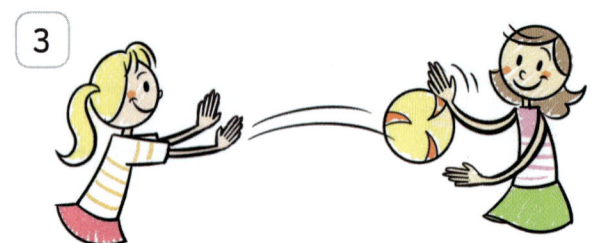

3. Brenda: **Push** / **Throw** the ball.
   May: **Pull** / **Catch** the ball.

4. **Kick** / **Hold** the ball.

5. **Push** / **Hit** the door.

6. **Push** / **Pull** the rope.

2 Read and match.

1. In tennis, hit
2. Bounce the
3. In baseball,
4. Kick the ball
5. Push
6. Pull the

a. rope.
b. in soccer.
c. a swing.
d. throw the ball.
e. ball in basketball.
f. the ball with a racket.

3 Read, choose, and write.

> bat   hit   person   racket   rope   stick   stones

In tennis, you hit the ball with a ¹ _____ . You need two people to play this sport. Swingball is a game you can play by yourself or with another ² _____ . There's a tennis ball on the end of a long ³ _____ . Hold the ⁴ _____ in your hand. When the ball comes round, ⁵ _____ it!

In India, children play games with seven small ⁶ _____ . They also play a game with a long ⁷ _____ and a small piece of wood.

Vocabulary challenge: sports

4 Look and write.

1. swimming _____
2. soccer _____
3. boxing _____
4. paddleboarding _____
5. ping-pong _____

gloves   net   goal   goggles   paddle

5 Look at the pictures in Activity 4. Read and write.

1. You wear them on your hands. _____
2. You wear them on your head. _____
3. You kick the ball into this. _____
4. You hit the ball over this with your bat. _____
5. You use this in the water. _____

Reading 2

1 Read *Sports Rules*. Choose and write.

| baseball | basketball | horseback riding |
| paddleboarding | water polo |

1 Don't take off your helmet. _____
2 Wear a life jacket. _____
3 You can hit the ball, but you can't kick it. _____
4 You can throw and catch the ball in the water. _____
5 You can bounce the ball. _____

2 Think and write.

1 What three things can your horse do when you go horseback riding?
   _____

2 In which three sports can you throw the ball?
   _____

3 In which two sports can you run?
   _____

4 In which sport can you swim?
   _____

3 Think of a brand new sport. Draw and write two rules.

My new sport is called _____.
Rules:
You can _____.
You can't _____.

Grammar 2

> **Can** I **play** soccer in the classroom?
> **Yes**, you **can**./**No**, you **can't**.
> You **can**/**can't** hit a ball in soccer.

1 Look, read, and write *Can, can,* or *can't*.

1. You .... play tennis with an egg!

2. You .... catch the ball in soccer.

3. .... you hit a ball with bats in the ocean?

4. You .... wear a helmet when you swim.

5. You .... throw the ball high in basketball.

6. You .... hit the ball with a bat in baseball.

97

2 Read and write *can* or *can't*.

POOL RULES

1 You .... push another person. ✗
2 You .... play with a ball. ✓
3 You .... eat or drink in the pool. ✗
4 You .... take off your swimming cap. ✗
5 You .... have swimming lessons. ✓
6 You .... jump in the pool. ✓
7 You .... run around the pool. It's dangerous. ✗

3 Write the words in order to make questions.

1 I / play / Can / in the classroom / field hockey
....?

2 I / badminton / play / Can / with my feet
....?

3 in soccer / catch / I / the ball / Can
....?

4 baseball / with my friends / play / Can / I
....?

5 kick / Can / the ball / I / at the bowling alley
....?

4 Look at Activity 3. Write answers with *Yes, you can* or *No, you can't*.

1 ....
2 ....
3 ....
4 ....
5 ....

Writing

1 **Read and match.**

1 I like swimming — Thomas

2 I like field hockey — Vicky

3 I like gymnastics — Kim

4 I like horseback riding — Mike

> **! Remember**
> 1 Read.
> 2 Get ready to write.
> 3 Now write!

a   because I love horses.

b   because you can bounce and jump.

c   because you can do it in the pool or in the ocean.

d   because I can play it with my friend in our yard.

2 **Draw a picture of a sportsperson. Then write about him/her.**

Name: ....

Sport: ....

I like him/her because ....

....

....

3 ✏️ **Write a description of your favorite sportsperson.**

My favorite sportsperson is ....

....

....

....

99

Now I Know

1 What sports can you play at this country park? Look and write.

Country Park

WATER SPORTS

p...................................... w......................................
p......................................

BALL SPORTS

b...................................... f......................................
h......................................
p...................................-
p...................................... b......................................

OUTDOOR SPORTS

h...................................... s......................................
r......................................

2 Read and circle two correct answers.

1 You can hit with it. **bat / door / racket**
2 You can't throw the ball when you play. **basketball / ping-pong / field hockey**
3 You can't pull it. **bat / rope / racket**
4 You can push it. **rope / swing / door**
5 You can bounce it. **stone / ball / balloon**
6 You can't kick the ball when you play. **tennis / swing / baseball**
7 You can hold it up high. **door / bat / racket**

3 Look, read, and write. Then complete for you.

★ What Are Your Skills? ★

Name	Sports	Dancing	Telling stories
Carla	✓	✗	✓
Muhwan	✗	✗	✓
Your name			

1 Carla .... good at sports, but Muhwan .... good at sports.
2 Carla and Muhwan .... good at telling stories, but they .... good at dancing.
3 I ....

Things I learn

1 Which sports do you know? Write six sports.

....
....

2 My new words! Draw and write.

3 My favorite words in this unit!

My three favorite words in this unit are ....

101

8 What makes us feel good?

What do you know?

1 What do you learn about in this unit? Read and complete.

We learn about why it's important to have healthy .... We also learn about which parts of the .... we use for different senses.

2 Watch the video. Read and circle.

1 Zebras eat **grass** / **meat**.
2 Zebras and koalas have **sharp** / **flat** teeth in the front.
3 Lions **chew** / **don't chew** their food.
4 Animals and people have **canines** / **molars** at the back of their mouths.
5 Animals **eat** / **don't eat** sweets.

3 Watch the video again. Read, choose, and write.

> canines   incisors   molars

1 Animals use .... to cut leaves and grass.
2 They use .... to chew their food.
3 Lions use .... to tear their meat into pieces.

4 Draw an open mouth. Draw molars, canines, and incisors.

102

Vocabulary 1

1 Read and circle.

1 Use your molars to **chew** / **rinse** your food.
2 Brush your teeth with **braces** / **a toothbrush**.
3 This **toothpaste** / **toothache** tastes nice!
4 I **chew** / **rinse** my mouth with **mouthwash** / **braces**.
5 My sister has **braces** / **toothbrush** on her teeth.
6 Are your teeth **chew** / **dirty**? Brush them!
7 Do you have a **toothpaste** / **toothache**? Go to the dentist.

2 Look and read. Write *yes* or *no*.

1 The boy wears braces. ....
2 The boy is rinsing his mouth with mouthwash. ....
3 The boy is using a blue toothbrush. ....
4 There's a picture of a clown on the toothpaste. ....
5 The puppy is chewing a toothbrush. ....

103

3 Look, read, and check (✓) or cross (✗).

1 This is toothpaste. ☐

2 This is a toothbrush. ☐

3 This is mouthwash. ☐

4 He has braces. ☐

5 He has a toothache. ☐

Word study: things, actions, and describing words

4 Complete the chart with the words in the box. Then add your own words.

| braces | chew | dirty | eat | rinse | toothbrush | white |

Things	Actions	Describing words

Reading 1

1 Read *Lots of Teeth!* Complete the sentences with numbers.

1 Some crocodiles have .... teeth.
2 Lions have .... teeth.
3 Humans have .... teeth.
4 Lions have .... canines.

2 Read *Lots of Teeth!* again. Check (✓) or cross (✗).

	Humans	Lions	Crocodiles
1 They chew their food.			
2 They don't chew their food.			
3 They grow new teeth again and again.			
4 They use their teeth to bite and cut food.			
5 They have molars.			
6 They have sharp teeth.			

3 Think and write.

1 What other animals have sharp teeth?

....

2 What animals chew their food?

....

3 Do babies chew food? Why/Why not?

....

105

Grammar 1

> You **should** = It's a good idea.
> You **shouldn't** = It's not a good idea.

1 Read and circle.

1 You **should** / **shouldn't** run in the street.
2 You **should** / **shouldn't** push another person.
3 You **should** / **shouldn't** do your homework every day.
4 You **should** / **shouldn't** say *Please* and *Thank you*.

2 Look, read, and write *should* or *shouldn't*.

1 He *shouldn't* eat a lot of candy.

2 I have a toothache. I _____ go to the dentist.

3 He _____ drink a lot of water.

4 He _____ go to bed early tonight.

5 He _____ ride his bike too fast!

6 They _____ play soccer close to the house.

3 Look, read, and write *should* or *shouldn't*.

1 The boy ___shouldn't___ feed the ducks.
2 The girl _____ play with a ball close to the ducks.
3 The dogs _____ walk on the flowers.
4 People _____ have a picnic on the grass.
  They _____ sit at the table.
5 People _____ put their trash in the trash can.

4 Read, circle, and write.

1 Help! I have a toothache!
  You **should** / **shouldn't** _____.
2 I'm always tired in the morning.
  You **should** / **shouldn't** _____.
3 I can't remember my new words.
  You **should** / **shouldn't** _____.
4 I want to be healthy.
  You **should** / **shouldn't** _____.

Vocabulary 2

1 Look, choose, and write.

> feel   hear   relax   smell   taste   touch

1 I can .... the ocean!

3 Mmm. I can .... vanilla and strawberries!

5 These flowers .... nice.

2 What can I .... ?

4 Don't .... it!

6 I can .... in this big, soft couch!

2 You're in your favorite place. What can you see/hear/taste/feel/smell?

I'm in the ocean. I can

108

3 Read and circle.

1 Don't **touch** / **relax** the stone. It's hot!
2 Listen. Can you **hear** / **smell** music?
3 I **taste** / **breathe** with my nose.
4 Does your tooth **relax** / **hurt**? You should go to the dentist.
5 Let's go to the beach. We can **taste** / **relax** in the sun.
6 Mmm. I can **smell** / **breathe** delicious food!
7 I don't like this food. It doesn't **taste** / **touch** nice.
8 I **smell** / **feel** with my fingers.

Vocabulary challenge: bathroom words

4 Look, choose, and write.

floss   shampoo   ~~shower gel~~   soap   sponge   towel

1 shower gel
2
3
4
5
6

5 Read and write. Use the words from Activity 4.

1 You use it to dry your body.
2 You use it to wash your hair.
3 You use it to wash your body. It's in a bottle.
4 You use it to wash your body. It's hard.

109

Reading 2

1 Read *What's That Noise?* Number the sentences in the correct order.

.... Leo eats a cheeseburger.
.... Leo has a toothache.
.... Leo hides under a blanket.
.... Leo can hear a noise.
.... Leo can smell his favorite food.
.... Clara gets some water for Leo.

2 Read *What's That Noise?* again and match.

1 Leo feels good
2 Leo loves
3 Clara gets a blanket for Leo because
4 Clara gets some water for Leo because
5 Leo hides under the blanket because

a he has a toothache.
b cheeseburgers.
c he feels cold.
d he can hear footsteps.
e when he's at home.

3 Read and find the words.

1 When there's no light. d ....
2 Something to use when you're cold. b ....
3 When your tooth hurts. t ....
4 The noise when someone is walking. f .... s
5 When you want something to eat. h ....

4 Think and write. What can you hear, see, and smell on a camping trip?

I can hear ....
I can see ....
I can smell ....

Grammar 2

Dad is baking. The bread **smells nice**!
My dinner **smells bad**!
The ice cream **tastes good**!
The ice cream **tastes bad**!

1 Look, read, and write *good* or *bad*.

1 The old ___fish___ smells _____.

3 I don't like _____. It tastes _____.

2 The _____ smells _____.

4 The _____ tastes _____!

2 How do you feel? Read and write.

1 I have a lot of homework.
   I feel bad.

2 I win a medal.
   _____

3 It's my birthday!
   _____

4 My tooth hurts.
   _____

5 I help other people.
   _____

6 My math homework is difficult.
   _____

111

I swim and I feel good. = I feel good **when** I swim.

3 Look, read, and write *good* or *bad*.

Maisie	it rains	☹
Daniel	there's soccer practice	☺
Lucy and Ryan	it's sunny	☺
Nadia	it's noisy	☹
Our teachers	we don't listen	☹

1 Maisie _feels bad_ when it rains.
2 Daniel _____ when there's soccer practice.
3 Lucy and Ryan _____ when it's sunny.
4 Nadia _____ when it's noisy.
5 Our teachers _____ when we don't listen.

4 Rewrite the sentences with *when*. Then write sentences for you.

1 I relax and I feel good.
   I feel good when I relax.
2 It's snowing and I feel cold.
   _____
3 I help my mom and I feel happy.
   _____
4 I go to bed late and I feel tired.
   _____
5 I play games and I feel happy.
   _____
6 I _____ and I feel bad.
   _____
7 I _____ and I feel good.
   _____

112

Writing

! Remember
1 Read.
2 Get ready to write.
3 Now write!

1 Match the words that rhyme.

1 dark   a day
2 hot   b lot
3 play   c course
4 horse   d park

2 How do you feel? Read, choose, and write.

bad   good   great   happy   sad   tired

MY DIARY

I feel .... when it's cold and dark.
I feel .... when it's a sunny day.
I feel .... when my friends come to play.
I feel .... when I play at the park.
I feel .... when it rains a lot.

3 Complete the poem. Use the words from Activity 2. Make sentences that rhyme.

I feel .... when it's a sunny day.
I feel .... when my friends come to play.
I feel .... when I play at the park.
But I feel .... when it's cold and dark.
I feel .... when it rains a lot.
But I feel .... when it ....
I feel .... when I ....
I feel .... when I'm .... !

Now I Know

1 Read, choose, and write.

> chew   dirty   mouthwash   rinse
> toothache   toothbrush   toothpaste

TAKE CARE OF YOUR TEETH!

- Do you feel bad when your teeth are ¹ .... ? Follow these rules for healthy, clean teeth.
- ² .... your food well when you eat.
- Put some ³ .... on your ⁴ ...., and brush your teeth.
  ⁵ .... your mouth with ⁶ ....
- Go to the dentist when you have a ⁷ ....

2 Read and match.

1 You can hear   a nose, mouth
2 You can touch with your   b in the sun, at the beach
3 You can smell   c music, singing
4 You can taste   d salt, sugar
5 You can relax   e fingers, hands
6 You can breathe through your   f flowers, bread

3 Read and write. Use *should* or *shouldn't*.

1 You .... wear a helmet when you ride a bike.
2 You .... do your homework.
3 You .... eat a lot of potato chips.
4 You .... be noisy in the classroom.
5 You .... eat a lot of fruit.
6 You .... push another person.

4 How do you feel? Read and write.

- my room is messy
- I take a bath
- I can't sleep at night
- I forget to do my homework
- I do well in my test
- I laugh and talk with my friends
- my mom cooks my favorite food
- my tooth hurts

1 I feel bad when my room is messy.
2
3
4
5
6
7
8

Things I learn

1 What makes you feel good? What makes you feel bad? Write six words.

Good: ....
Bad: ....

2 My new words! Draw and write.

3 My favorite words in this unit!

My three favorite words in this unit are ....

9 How are the seasons different?

What do you know?

1 What do you learn about in this unit? Read and complete.

We learn about the twelve _____ of the year and the four _____ .

2 Watch the video. Read, choose, and write.

bottom   line   month   numbers   rain

1 What's the average rainfall for each _____ ?
2 Let's draw a _____ graph.
3 We write the months on the _____ .
4 We write the _____ on the side.
5 The y axis shows the number of millimeters of _____ .

3 Watch the video again. Read and circle.

1 January: **60 / 80** millimeters of rain.
2 March: **55 / 65** millimeters.
3 April: **55 / 60** millimeters.
4 July: **60 / 70** millimeters.
5 October: **85 / 90** millimeters.
6 December: **80 / 85** millimeters.

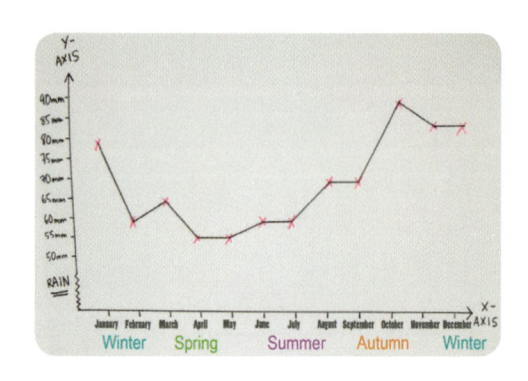

4 How often does it rain in your country? Which month has the most rain?

116

Vocabulary 1

1 Write the missing letters.

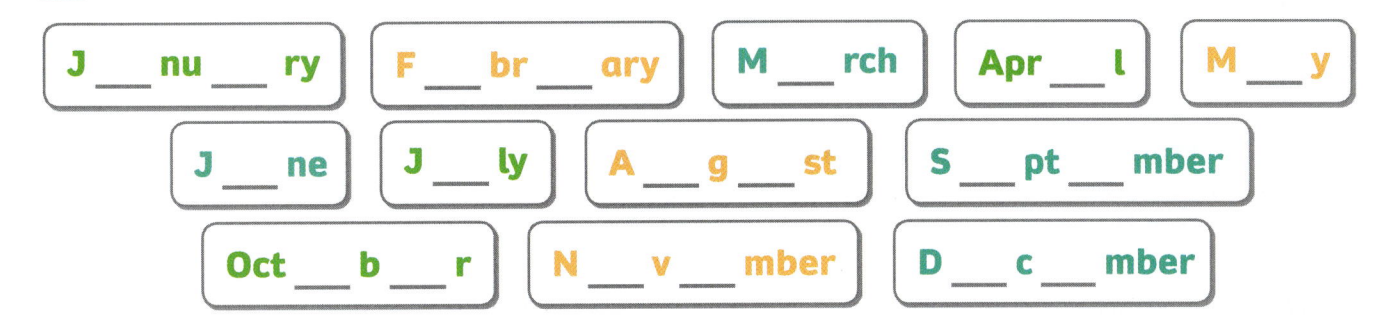

J__nu__ry   F__br__ary   M__rch   Apr__l   M__y

J__ne   J__ly   A__g__st   S__pt__mber

Oct__b__r   N__v__mber   D__c__mber

2 Look and write the letters in order.

1. _____   r F a r / u e y b

2. _____   l A r / p i

3. _____   g s A u / t u

4. _____   r b c e / o O t

5. _____   b c r e / D m e e

3 Read and write.

1 This month has only three letters. ....
2 This month has only 28 days (or 29). ....
3 This month has six letters. ....
4 This month has nine letters. ....

4 What about you? Read and write.

1 My birthday is in ....
2 My best friend's birthday is in ....
3 The first day of summer vacation is in ....
4 The first day of a new school year is in ....
5 My favorite month is .... , because ....
....

Word study: capital letters

5 Write the missing letters. Which ones are capital letters?

| a   d   m   p   s   t |

1 ___ hursday
2 ___ ecember
3 ___ andals
4 ___ onth
5 ___ ablo
6 ___ ugust

6 Read and write the letters that should be capital letters.

juan: hello. i'm juan, from mexico.
kathy: my name is kathy. i'm from canada. when's your birthday?
juan: it's in september! and yours?
kathy: october!

Reading 1

1 Read *Larry the Lemur* and match.

1.
2.
3.
4.

a **December**
b **September**
c **February**
d **June**

2 Read *Larry the Lemur* again. Choose and write.

| cold | fat | flowers | June | sleeps | thin |

1 In February, Larry eats .... and fruit.
2 Larry can't find food when it's ....
3 When it's hot, Larry's tail gets ....
4 Larry is tired in ....
5 From June to November, Larry ....
6 In December, Larry's tail is ....

3 What food do you eat when it's hot and when it's cold? Draw and write.

When it's hot, I eat ....
....

When it's cold, I eat ....
....

119

Grammar 1

always ★★★★
often ★★★☆
sometimes ★★☆☆
never ☆☆☆☆

1 Look, read, and circle.

Ali's Schedule

Monday	Tuesday	Wednesday	Thursday	Friday
walk to school	walk to school	go to school by bus	walk to school	walk to school
guitar practice	guitar practice	guitar practice	guitar practice	guitar practice
	watch TV			play basketball

1 He **always / often** walks to school.
2 He **often / sometimes** goes to school by bus.
3 He **never / often** goes to school by car.
4 He **always / sometimes** has guitar practice.
5 He **often / sometimes** plays basketball.
6 He **sometimes / always** watches TV.

2 Read and write. Use *never*, *always*, *sometimes*, or *often*.

Yolanda's Hobbies

My favorite sport is soccer. I play every day of the week. I don't like playing video games, so I don't play them. I do judo twice a month. On weekdays, I read a book before bed.

1 Yolanda _____ plays soccer.
2 She _____ plays video games.
3 She _____ reads a book.
4 She _____ does judo.

3 Look, read, and write *sometimes*, *often*, or *always*.

When it's sunny, do you … ?
1 go swimming ✓✓✓
2 wear sandals ✓✓✓✓✓
3 wear a coat ✗
4 sleep all day ✓✓

When it's rainy, do you … ?
5 relax on the beach ✗
6 take an umbrella ✓✓✓✓✓
7 walk to school ✗
8 go to the park ✓✓

When it's sunny …
1 I .... go swimming.
2 I .... wear sandals.
3 I .... wear a coat.
4 I .... sleep all day.

When it's rainy …
5 I .... relax on the beach.
6 I .... take an umbrella.
7 I .... walk to school.
8 I .... go to the park.

4 Write the words in order.

1 it's sunny / I often / when / play soccer
   ....

2 Susan / eats chicken soup / usually / when she has a cold
   ....

3 when it's rainy / My brother / books / sometimes reads
   ....

4 video games / play / We never / in the morning
   ....

5 Write for you.

1 I often .... when it's sunny.
2 I usually .... when I have a cold.
3 I .... read books when it's rainy.
4 I never .... in the morning.

Vocabulary 2

1 Look and write the missing letters.

1. w __ __ d
2. __ __ m __ r
3. N __ t __
4. __ __ n t __ __
5. __ __ u __ h
6. __ p __ __ __ g

2 Read and circle.

1. In the **winter / summer**, we go ice skating outside.
2. In the **spring / winter**, there are a lot of flowers in the yard.
3. Look at the map of the world. Is your country in the **South / seasons**?
4. I live in the **spring / north** of the country.
5. There are many different countries in the **seasons / world**.
6. In the **winter / fall**, the leaves change color.
7. How many **seasons / world** are there?
8. I love the **seasons / summer**, because it's nice and hot.

3 Read and write the season.

1. The leaves are orange, yellow, and red. ....
2. There are no leaves on the trees. ....
3. Small leaves are growing on the trees. ....
4. The leaves are big and green. ....

4 Read and write the letters in order.

The ¹ drowl _world_ is a very big place! Many different animals live in the ² orNth _North_ and the ³ othSu _South_. Different countries have different ⁴ esasnos _seasons_, too. My favorite is the ⁵ muserm _summer_, when it's hot. In the ⁶ terwin _winter_ it's often cold. Sometimes it snows in my country. In the ⁷ alfl _fall_ the leaves on the trees change color. They're orange, yellow, and red. Then in the ⁸ ingspr _spring_, everything becomes green again.

Vocabulary challenge: climate

5 Look, choose, and write.

dry   polar   temperate   tropical

1 tropical
2 dry
3 temperate
4 polar

6 Read and write. Use the words from Activity 5.

1 This climate is nice and warm. _temperate_
2 This climate is hot. It rains a lot. _tropical_
3 This climate is very cold. _polar_
4 This climate is hot. It sometimes rains. _dry_

123

Reading 2

1 Read *North and South* and match.

1. When it's winter in the North,
2. The equator is
3. The Northern Hemisphere is
4. When it's fall in the South,
5. When it's hot,
6. When it's cold,
7. When it's January in the South,

a. on the other side of the Southern Hemisphere.
b. children swim in the ocean.
c. around the middle of the world.
d. children play in the snow.
e. it's summer in the South.
f. it's January in the North.
g. it's spring in the North.

2 Read *North and South* again and write.

1. When it's July in the North, it's _____ in the South.
2. When it's _____ in the North, it's winter in the South.
3. When it's _____, the leaves become orange.
4. When it's _____, the leaves become green again.
5. In the North, it's _____ in December, January, and February.
6. In the South, _____ is the middle of the summer.

3 Read and circle. Then draw the weather.

It's the Southern Hemisphere.
It's February. It's **winter / summer**.

It's the Northern Hemisphere.
It's February. It's **winter / summer**.

Grammar 2

How often does it rain?

It **always** / **often** / **sometimes** / **never** rains.

How often does it snow?

It **always** / **often** / **sometimes** / **never** snows.

1 Read and circle.

1 **How often** / **How many** does it rain in winter?
   It often rains in the winter.
2 How often **do** / **does** it snow in summer?
   It never snows in the summer.
3 How often **does** / **is** it rain in spring?
   It sometimes rains in the spring.
4 How often does it **snow** / **rain** in fall?
   It never snows in the fall.

2 Read and write.

Sula: ¹ How often does it snow in summer?
Tony: It ² _____ snows in summer. (✗)
Sula: How ³ _____ does it rain in fall?
Tony: It ⁴ _____ rains in fall. (☆☆)
Sula: How often ⁵ _____ snow in winter?
Tony: It ⁶ _____ snows in winter. (☆☆☆☆)
Sula: ⁷ _____ it rain in spring?
Tony: It ⁸ _____ rains in spring. (☆☆)
Sula: ⁹ _____ it rain in winter?
Tony: It ¹⁰ _____ rains in winter. (☆☆☆)

3 Write questions.

1 How often / rain / August?
   How often does it rain in August?

2 How often / snow / January?

3 How often / rain / November?

4 How often / snow / December?

5 How often / rain / April?

4 Look at Activity 3. Read and write *always*, *often*, *sometimes*, or *never*.

1 It .... in August.
2 It .... in January.
3 It .... in November.
4 It .... in December.
5 It .... in April.

5 Think and write. How often does it rain and snow in your country? In which month or season?

It .... snows in ....

It .... rains in ....

Writing

1 Rewrite the sentences with *It* or *It's*.

> **Remember**
> 1 Read.
> 2 Get ready to write.
> 3 Now write!

Weather and Seasons in Costa Rica

I live in Costa Rica. It's very close to the equator.

1 The weather is usually very hot here.
It's usually very hot here.

2 The weather sometimes gets cool.
....

3 The weather is cooler between November and January.
....

4 The weather is very hot from March to May.
....

2 Draw a picture of your favorite season. Then write for you.

My favorite season is ....

This season is in the months of
....

What's the weather like in this season?

It's ....

During this season I usually
....

3 Write about your favorite season and the weather.

My country: ....

My favorite season: ....

The weather in this season is ....

....

I usually ....

127

Now I Know

1 Write the missing letters. Then number the months in the correct order.

.... J ___ ___ e
.... Ap ___ ___ ___
.... D ___ ___ ___ m ___ ___ r
.... A ___ ___ ___ st
..*1*..... J *a* n *u* ar *y*
.... N ___ ___ e ___ b ___ ___
.... S ___ ___ ___ e ___ ___ ___ r
.... M ___ ___
.... Fe ___ ___ ___ ___ ___ ry
.... O ___ ___ b ___ ___
.... J ___ ___ y
.... M ___ ___ h

2 Look and write the seasons.

1 .... 2 .... 3 .... 4 ....

3 What do you do when it's hot and when it's cold? Read and write.

When it's hot, I always .... I often .... I never ....
When it's cold, I sometimes ....
I always ...., but I never ....

128

4 Read and write *always*, *often*, *sometimes*, or *never*.

1 It _____ rains in the rain forest. (☆☆☆)
2 It _____ snows in the desert. (✗)
3 It _____ rains on the savannah. (☆☆)
4 It _____ snows in the Arctic. (☆☆☆☆)
5 It's _____ hot in December in Australia. (☆☆☆)
6 I _____ swim in the summer. (☆☆☆☆)

Things I learn

1 Which season is it in your country? Read and write.

1 In March, it's _____ .
2 In December, it's _____ .
3 In July, it's _____ .
4 In October, it's _____ .

2 My new words! Draw and write.

3 My favorite words in this unit!

My three favorite words in this unit are _____ .

10 How are we all different?

What do you know?

1 What do you learn about in this unit? Read and complete.

We learn about family and friends – what they look like, and how they act.
We learn to talk about how we're the same or ....

2 🎬 10-1 BBC Watch the video. Look, choose, and write.

brother   grandpa   granny   parents   sister

1 ....
2 ....
3 ....
4 ....
5 ....

3 🎬 10-1 BBC Watch the video again. Circle **T** (true) or **F** (false).

1 Grandpa and Granny Smith are the oldest people in the family.   T   F
2 Miranda's brother is older than her.   T   F
3 Brothers and sisters sit on the same branch.   T   F
4 The oldest people are at the bottom.   T   F

4 Draw your family tree.

130

Vocabulary 1

1 Read and circle.

1 Tina's very **shy / chatty**. She talks all the time!
2 That's a beautiful drawing. You're very **grumpy / creative**!
3 When Mia feels tired, she's **active / grumpy**. Look at her angry face!
4 Rosie doesn't like talking to people. She's a bit **kind / shy**.
5 People feel good when you say **active / kind** things to them.
6 Zachary's a **shy / hardworking** student. He always studies.
7 Thank you for carrying my heavy bag. You're very **grumpy / helpful**.
8 Ben's very **creative / active**. He plays a lot of sports every day.

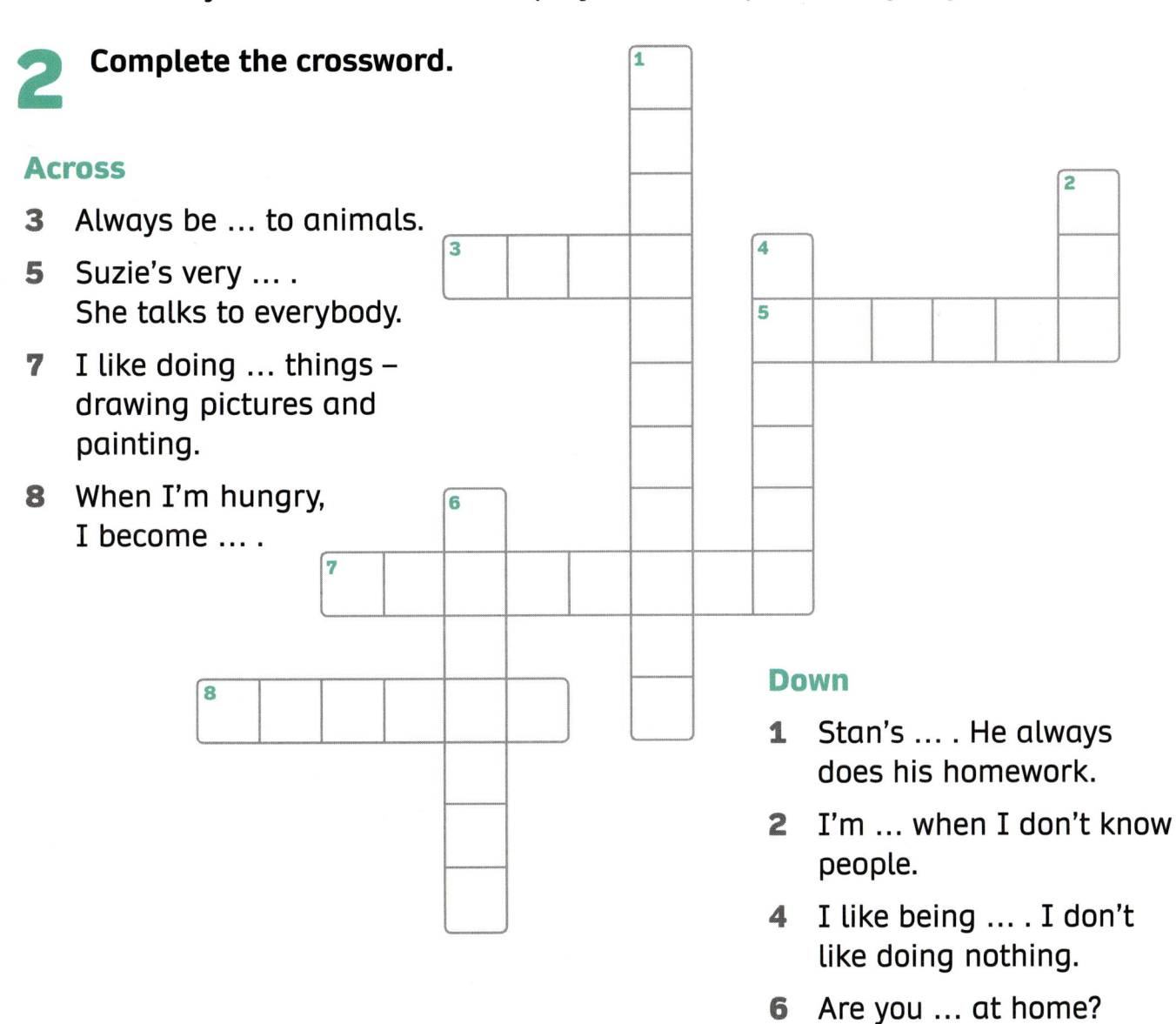

2 Complete the crossword.

Across

3 Always be … to animals.
5 Suzie's very … . She talks to everybody.
7 I like doing … things – drawing pictures and painting.
8 When I'm hungry, I become … .

Down

1 Stan's … . He always does his homework.
2 I'm … when I don't know people.
4 I like being … . I don't like doing nothing.
6 Are you … at home?

131

3 Look, choose, and write.

| active | chatty | creative | grumpy | helpful | shy |

1 ....
2 ....
3 ....
4 ....
5 ....
6 ....

4 What about you? Read, choose, and write.

| creative | grumpy | hardworking | kind | shy |

I'm .... , ... , and ....
I'm not ....

Word study: actions and describing words

5 Complete the chart with the words in the box. Add two more examples for each.

| act | active | chat | chatty |
| hardworking | help | helpful | work |

Actions	Describing words
....	....
....	....
....	....

Reading 1

1 Read *Mr. Blake and the Ball* and match.

1 Alex is   a chatty.
2 Mr. Blake is   b hardworking.
3 Alex's parents are   c creative.
4 Annie is   d active.
5 Grandma is   e grumpy.

2 Read *Mr. Blake and the Ball* again and write.

1 Mr. Blake is Alex's _____ . He lives next door.
2 Alex kicks his ball into Mr. Blake's _____ .
3 Annie's busy. She's _____ a picture.
4 Grandma's talking on the _____ .
5 Mr. Blake can't _____ very well.

3 Think and write.

1 Why does Alex say that he's brave? _____
2 Do you know your neighbors? _____
3 Do you talk to your neighbors? _____

4 Draw and write about your neighbor.

This is my neighbor. **He's / She's** _____ .

Grammar 1

Me: 8

My brother: 12

My sister: 3

I'm **younger** than my brother.

I'm **older** than my sister.

1 Look, read, and circle.

Jess   Bella   Ryan

1 Jess is **taller** / **shorter** than Bella.
2 Ryan is **taller** / **shorter** than Bella.
3 Bella's hair is **longer** / **shorter** than Jess's hair.
4 Jess's hair is **shorter** / **longer** than Bella's hair.
5 Ryan is **older** / **younger** than Jess.
6 Bella is **older** / **younger** than Ryan.

2 Look, read, and write.

1 The blue ruler is .... the yellow ruler.
2 The yellow ruler is .... the blue ruler.

3 Mom is .... Dad.
4 Dad is .... Mom.

5 The girl is .... the boy.
6 The boy is .... the girl.

3 Look and read. Write *yes* or *no*.

1 Dad is shorter than Mom. ....
2 The tree is taller than Dad. ....
3 Grandpa is older than Mom and Dad. ....
4 The girl is younger than the boy. ....
5 Mom's hair is shorter than Grandpa's hair. ....

4 Choose and write about you and your friends.

longer   older   shorter   taller   younger

1 I'm taller than Pedro.
2
3
4
5
6

135

Vocabulary 2

1 Look, read, and circle.

1. Grandpa has a **beard** / **mustache**.

3. My brother has **curly** / **straight** hair.

5. My hair is **brown** / **blonde** – and Mom's is, too!

2. My sister has **straight** / **wavy** hair.

4. My friend has **straight** / **curly** hair.

6. Her dad has a **beard** / **mustache**.

2 Read and write.

1. My grandpa doesn't have a beard. He has a _____.
2. My hair isn't curly and it isn't wavy. It's _____.
3. Your hair isn't dark. It's _____.
4. My neighbor has no hair. He's _____.
5. When I'm surprised, I raise my _____.
6. Her hair isn't straight and it isn't wavy. It's _____.

136

3 🎧 05 📋 Listen and color.

Vocabulary challenge: disabilities

4 Look, choose, and write the missing letters.

> blind   deaf   mute

1 m ___ ___ ___

2 b ___ ___ n ___

3 ___ ___ ___ f

5 Look at Activity 4. Read and write.

1 Which word means "cannot hear"? ....
2 Which word means "cannot speak"? ....
3 Which word means "cannot see"? ....

137

Reading 2

1 Read *How to Make a Family Album*. Number the sentences in the correct order.

.... Write descriptions in the scrapbook next to the pictures.

.... Collect pictures of all the people on your list.

.... Ask them questions about other people in the family.

.... Make a list of all the people you know in your family.

.... Stick the pictures in a scrapbook.

2 Read *How to Make a Family Album* again and circle **T** (true) or **F** (false).

1. It's a good idea to stick a lot of pictures on one page.   T   F
2. Ellen was Walter's great-grandmother.   T   F
3. Ellen Bright's hair was straight.   T   F
4. Ellen was kind.   T   F
5. Walter Bright's eyebrows were brown.   T   F

3 Think and write.

1. Do you take pictures of your family? ....
2. Do you have family albums at home? ....
3. Why do people keep family albums? ....

4 Read, circle, and write. Then draw.

My **grandmother's** / **grandfather's** name is
....

This is a picture of **his** / **her** favorite thing.

138

Grammar 2

I'm 8 now. Last year I **was** 7.
He's 9 now. Last year he **was** 8.
She's 10 now. Last year she **was** 9.

We're 11 now. Last year we **were** 10.
You're 12 now. Last year you **were** 11.

1 Read and circle.

1 Yesterday it **was** / **were** hot.
2 On my birthday last month, I **was** / **were** ten years old.
3 You **was** / **were** at home yesterday.
4 Last year we **was** / **were** in 2nd grade.
5 Yesterday the children **was** / **were** hardworking.
6 Last year our teacher **was** / **were** Miss Brown.

2 Read and match.

1 He's happy now.
2 We're tall now.
3 My plant is tall now.
4 They're active now.
5 You're chatty now.
6 I'm older now.

a They were lazy last week.
b You were shy on Monday.
c He was grumpy yesterday.
d I was younger last year.
e It was short last month.
f We were short last year.

3 Read and write the opposites.

1 My new sneakers are white. My old sneakers were _____ .
2 The house is very _____ . Once, it was new.
3 I was very lazy, but I'm _____ these days.
4 Tina is _____ with new people, but chatty once she knows them.

4 Look, read, and write *was* or *were*.

My First Day at School

I remember my first day at school very well. I **¹** .... six years old. There **²** .... 24 other children in my class. My first teacher **³** .... Miss Green. She **⁴** .... very kind and helpful. Her hair **⁵** .... long and straight. Her eyes **⁶** .... blue. Her classes **⁷** .... always fun. I remember the classroom, too. There **⁸** .... a lot of pictures on the walls, books to read, and games to play. It **⁹** .... a fun place!

5 Think about your first day at school. Draw and write.

My first teacher ....

....

My classmates ....

....

My classroom ....

....

Writing

1 Read and write the two describing words in the correct order.

1 My mother has _____ hair. (blonde, wavy)
2 She has _____ eyes. (brown, big)
3 We have a _____ dog. (friendly, black)
4 Today I'm wearing my _____ cap. (red, new)

Remember
1 Read.
2 Get ready to write.
3 Now write!

2 Read, circle, and write words to describe yourself and someone in your family.

How I Look

Now

I'm **tall** / **short**.

I have _____ hair.

_____

When I was three years old

I was _____ .

My hair was _____

_____ .

My _____

How he/she looks

He / She is _____

_____

_____ .

What he/she is like

He / She is _____

_____

_____ .

3 Draw a picture of someone you know. Then write a description of them using the words from Activity 2.

141

Now I Know

1 Read and match the opposites.

1 long
2 short
3 big
4 curly
5 chatty
6 young
7 black
8 lazy

a white
b old
c shy
d hardworking
e short
f small
g tall
h straight

2 Look, read, and write.

1

He has a _____.

2

He's _____,
and he has a _____.

3 Look, choose, and write.

I'm nine!   Mia
I'm eight! Eve

| longer   older   shorter |
| taller   younger |

1 Mia's hair is _____ than Eve's hair.
2 Mia is _____ than Eve.
3 Eve is _____ than Mia.
4 Mia is _____ than Eve.
5 Eve is _____ than Mia.

4 Look and write about the weather yesterday and today. Then write about the weather in your town/city yesterday and today.

Yesterday   Today

Yesterday it ¹ .... sunny. The sky ² .... blue and there ³ .... some clouds. Today the sky ⁴ .... gray, and ⁵ .... raining.

....
....

Things I learn

1 What words do you use to describe people? Write eight words.

....
....

2 My new words! Draw and write.

3 My favorite words in this unit!

My three favorite words in this unit are ....

11 How do we solve problems?

What do you know?

1 What do you learn about in this unit? Read and complete.

We learn how to do math ....

2 Watch the video. Choose and write.
11-1 BBC

chair   inside door   outside door   stairs   table   window

1 ....
2 ....
3 ....
4 ....
5 ....
6 ....

3 Draw and label a plan of your classroom.

Vocabulary 1

1 Read and circle.

1. You **add** / **measure** with a ruler.
2. I can do this **measure** / **sum**. It's easy!
3. Two **plus** / **minus** two = four.
4. Ten **plus** / **minus** two = eight.
5. Five plus five **sum** / **equals** ten.
6. **Subtract** / **Add** two to six. What do you get? Eight.
7. **Subtract** / **Add** one from five. What do you get? Four.
8. I love doing math **problems** / **measures**!

2 Read, choose, and write. Then draw.

add   equals   minus   ~~plus~~   subtract

1. 5 __plus__ 5 _____ 10

2. 5 _____ 2 = 3

3. Katie has three bananas.
   _____ one more.
   Now she has four bananas.

4. There are six strawberries. Ben eats one.
   _____ one from six.
   Now there are five strawberries.

145

3 Look, read, and write.

1 She's _____ with a ruler.

3 She's _____ the numbers.

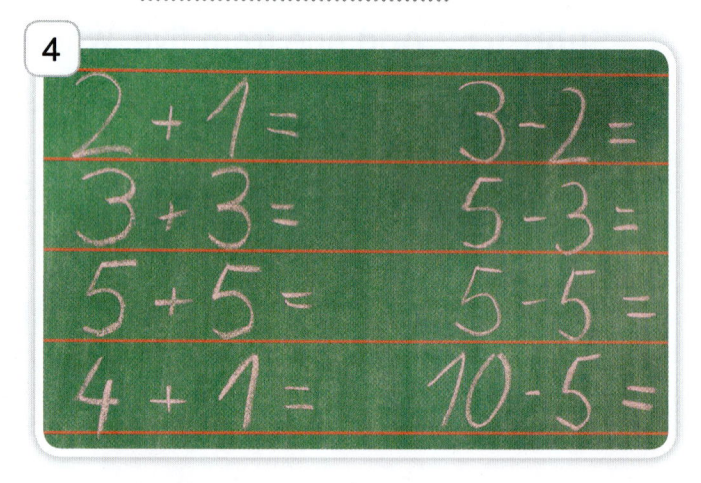

2 He's _____ the numbers.

4 We're doing _____ .

Word study: q

4 Read these words aloud. Then circle the letter that follows *q* and write.

equals   question   quick   quiet   quiz

Letter *q* is always followed by letter _____ .

5 Write the missing letters. Then match to the opposites.

1 ___ ___ ick   a noisy
2 ___ ___ iet   b answer
3 ___ ___ een   c king
4 ___ ___ estion   d slow

Reading 1

1 Read *Math Problems!* Look, read, and write.

1. Whose lunchbox is this – Sarah's or Joel's?

   ....

2. Whose candies are these – Jonny's or his sister's?

   ....

3. How many cars are a gift from Great-grandmother?

   ....

4. Whose books are these – Grace's or her brother's?

   ....

2 Read and write. Then do the sums.

1. Jonny has .... candies. His brother and his friend, Roy, like candies, too. Jonny gives his brother .... candies. Then he gives Roy .... candies. How many candies does Jonny have now? ....

2. Grace has .... books. Her sister likes books, too. Grace gives her .... books. How many books does Grace have now? ....

3. Oliver has .... toy cars. His friend, Danny, gives him .... toy cars. How many toy cars does Oliver have now? ....

3 What about you? Read and circle.

I **like** / **don't like** doing problems and sums. They're **fun** / **difficult**.

147

Grammar 1

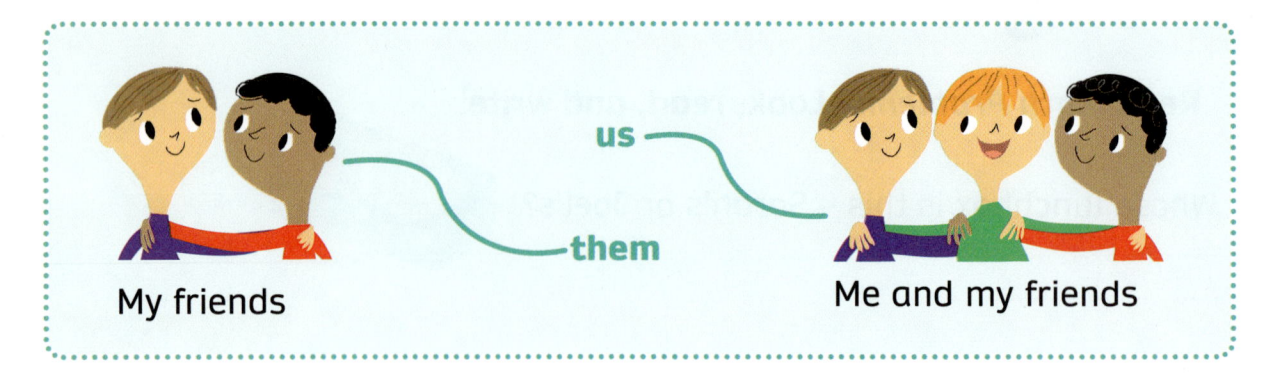

My friends — us / them — Me and my friends

1 Look, read, and circle.

1. Please help **them / us**!

2. Ducks shouldn't eat bread. Please don't feed **her / them**.

3. My friends are over there, Grandpa! Let's talk to **me / them**.

4. Can you show **us / them** the way to the station, please?

2 Read and write *me, us, her,* or *them*.

1. Mom says, "Let's buy the children some ice cream."
   Mom says, "Let's buy _____ some ice cream."

2. Please tell me and my friends what the time is.
   Please tell _____ what the time is.

3. Every year, I paint my grandmother a picture.
   Every year, I paint _____ a picture.

4. On the last day of the term, our teacher throws me and my classmates a party.
   On the last day of the term, our teacher throws _____ a party.

5. "What's the time?" the children ask me.
   The children ask _____ what the time is.

3 Read and write *me, us, her,* or *them* and the words in parentheses.

1. I don't know how to open this window. (show)
   Please _show me_ how to open the window.

2. My friends and I are lost. (help)
   Please _____.

3. Those children are hungry. (give)
   Let's _____ some food.

4. I don't understand this word. (tell)
   Please _____ what this word means.

5. She want to learn how to do these sums. (teach)
   Please _____ how to do these sums.

4 Write for you.

1. In what way do you help your parents/friends?
   I help them clean the house.

2. What does your teacher help you and your classmates do?
   My teacher helps _____.

Vocabulary 2

1 Look, read, and check (✓) or cross (✗).

1. This is a maze. ☐

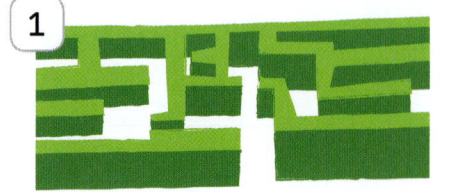

2. This is the exit. ☐

3. This is the entrance. ☐

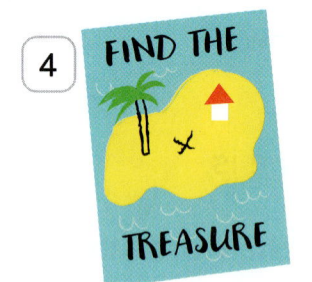

4. This is a treasure hunt. ☐

5. She's lost. ☐

2 Draw a maze. Hide some treasure in it. Draw the entrance and the exit. Then give it to a friend. Can they solve the puzzle?

3 Read, choose, and write.

> clue   entrance   exit   hide   lost
> maze   solve   treasure hunt

1. Do our _____ and find the treasure! It's somewhere inside this big _____ !
2. START HERE at the _____ .
3. **Tomas:** Where are you, George?
   George: I don't know where I am! I'm _____ !
4. Look. Here's a _____ . It will help us.
5. Don't _____ , Pedro! We can see you.
6. Come on, we have to _____ the problem!
7. This is the _____ . You GO OUT here.

Vocabulary challenge: problem solving

4 Look, read, and circle.

1. riddle / puzzle
2. secret / quiz
3. puzzle / secret
4. secret / riddle

What has bark but no bite?

5 Read and write. Use the words from Activity 4.

1. If your friend tells you a _____ , don't repeat it!
2. You guess what your friend is thinking about. It's a _____ .
3. You put different pieces together to show a bigger picture. It's a _____ .
4. You need to choose the correct answers. It's a _____ .

Reading 2

1 Read *Escape the Classroom!* and circle **T** (true) or **F** (false).

1. The treasure is a key to the cupboard.   T   F
2. Find the correct animal to open the cupboard door.   T   F
3. Kangaroo mothers carry their babies in their arms.   T   F
4. A door can be an entrance or an exit.   T   F
5. Blue and yellow mixed together makes green.   T   F

2 Read *Escape the Classroom!* again and write.

1. The treasure hunt is in the ....
2. The treasure is a ....
3. How can you find the treasure? .... the clues!
4. The treasure is in a green ....

3 Read the clue and solve the riddle. Then write your own clue and the answer.

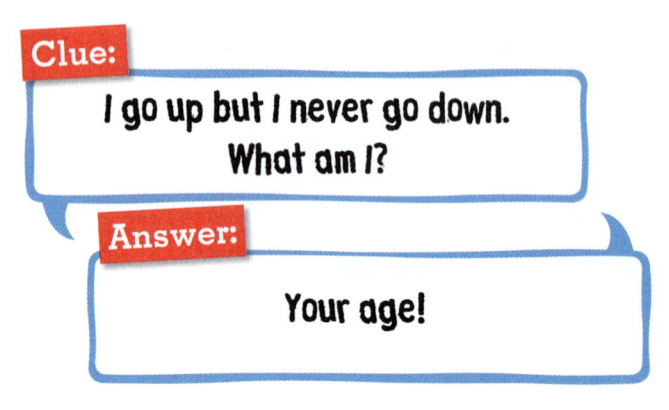

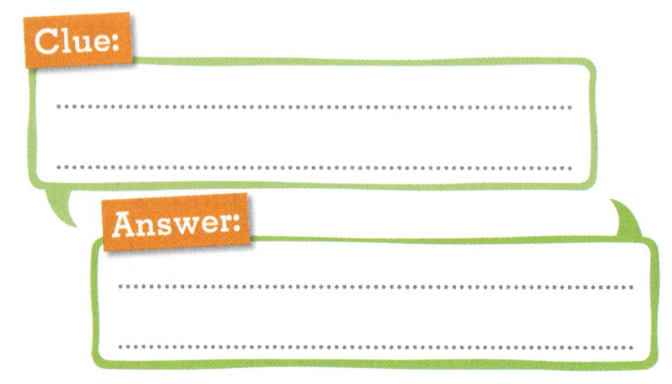

Clue: I go up but I never go down. What am I?

Answer: Your age!

Clue: ....

Answer: ....

152

Grammar 2

> I **can hear** some birds.
>
> I **can't see** my friend.
>
> They **can see** my friends and me.
>
> They **can't hear** the train.

1 Read and circle.

1 Are you making a cake? I can **smell** / **touch** it.
2 You **can** / **can't** walk on the sand. It's hot.
3 Is there any salt in this food? I can't **hear** / **taste** it.
4 There are some monkeys in that tree. Can you **see** / **taste** them?
5 Those flowers are beautiful. Can I **touch** / **touched** them?
6 Let's hide under the bed. Then our friends **can** / **can't** see us.

2 Read and match.

1 You can see it, but you can't touch the top.
2 I can hear it.
3 We can smell it and see it, but we can't touch it.
4 You can see it, but you can't touch it.
5 I can taste them.
6 We can hear them.

a footsteps
b the sky
c cupcakes
d a tall building
e the ocean
f smoke

3 Read and write. Then find the hidden word.

1 We're hiding. Mom and Dad can't see ... .
2 Don't shout! They can ... us.
3 These fruits look nice. Can I taste ...?

4 🎧 📋 Listen and check (✓).

1 What can Johnny hear?

a ☐   b ☐   c ☐

2 What can Betty see?

a ☐   b ☐   c ☐

3 What can Eva smell?

a ☐   b ☐   c ☐

5 💡 Read, draw, and write.

1 I can smell, touch, and taste this fruit.

2 It's in my living room. I can see, hear, and touch it.

Writing

> **! Remember**
> 1 Read.
> 2 Get ready to write.
> 3 Now write!

1 Read and match.

1 I love sports,
2 I enjoy solving problems,
3 A lot of fruit tastes sweet,
4 I like doing sums,
5 Some words are not easy to spell,

a for example, *laugh* and *difficult*.
b for example, basketball and tennis.
c for example, finding the exit in a maze.
d for example, oranges and apples.
e for example, adding and subtracting.

2 Think of a math problem. Read and write.

Math Time!

1 Choose a number. Write it here. ....
2 Choose a symbol (plus/minus) and write it here. ....
3 Choose another number. Write it here. ....
4 What's your total? Write it here. ....
5 Now think of an object to use in your problem, for example, apples, pens, toys, or books. Write the word(s) here. ....
6 Think of characters and a situation. Why are they subtracting or adding objects?
....

3 Write your problem. Draw pictures to show the characters, objects, and the situation.

155

Now I Know

1 Complete the crossword.

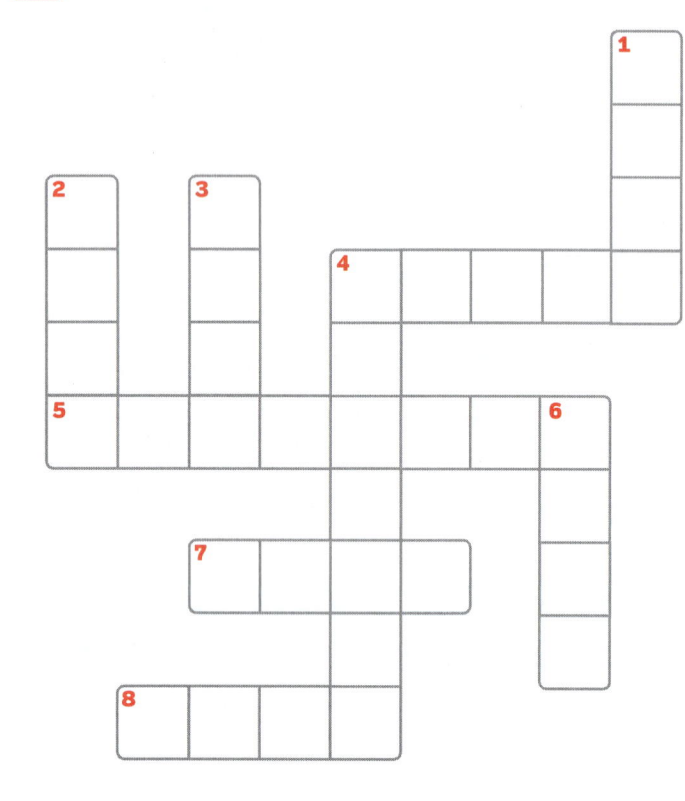

Across
4 The sign for subtracting.
5 You go in here.
7 The sign for adding.
8 People can't see you when you do this.

Down
1 You do these in math.
2 You can get lost easily in this place.
3 You don't know your way to a place.
4 You do this with a ruler.
6 You go out here.

2 Find and circle six words.

naaddoremeasurelasequalsintcluerdasolventisubtractugo

3 Read and write.

1 There are twelve apples in the tree. Jacinto eats one, and Leon eats two. How many apples are there on the tree now?

Write the sum.

2 It's Jamal's birthday. His parents give him a present. His friends give him three presents. How many presents does he have?

Write the sum.

4 Read, choose, and write *them*, *it*, or *us*.

~~hear~~   see   smell   taste   touch

1 Is that music? I can _____hear it_____ .
2 Are you making hot chocolate? I can _____ .
3 Look at the oranges at the top of the tree.
   They're too high. I can't _____ .
4 Is there sugar in this tea? I can't _____ .
5 Let's hide here. Then they can't _____ !

Things I learn

1 What do you do to solve problems? Write four words.

....

2 My new words! Draw and write.

3 My favorite words in this unit!

My three favorite words in this unit are _____.

157

12 Why is it good to be outdoors?

What do you know?

1 What do you learn about in this unit? Read and complete.

We learn how to talk about things we can find and do _____ .

2 ▶ BBC Watch the video. Read, choose, and write.

> big   cat   girl   last   shell

1 It's difficult to take photos on a tablet because a tablet is _____ .
2 The children took photos of a _____ and a _____ .
3 The _____ is his boat.
4 Their _____ photo is a close-up.

3 ▶ BBC Watch the video again. Number the tips in the order you hear them.

_____ Hold the tablet still.
_____ When it's dark, use the flash.
_____ Use zoom for close-ups.
_____ Use a tripod.
_____ Talk about the photos and what to have in them.
_____ Plan and draw the photos.

4 💡 Think about your favorite picture. What/Who is in it? Where are they? What are they doing?

Vocabulary 1

1 Look, read, and circle.

1 There's a **meadow** / **rock** with a lot of flowers.
2 There's a lake with **ponds** / **hills** around it.
3 There are some big **rocks** / **grass** in the lake.
4 There's a boat on the **meadow** / **sand**.
5 There's a small **grass** / **pond** with **wildlife** / **meadow** in it.
6 A dog is lying on the **grass** / **lake**.

2 Read and circle two correct answers.

1 You can go fishing in a **pond** / **meadow** / **lake**.
2 You can relax on the **pond** / **grass** / **sand**.
3 At the beach, you can see **sand** / **lakes** / **wildlife**.
4 Flowers grow in **rocks** / **a meadow** / **the hills**.
5 I wear sandals to walk on the hot **rocks** / **pond** / **sand**.
6 Let's go for a walk in the **lake** / **hills** / **meadow**.

3 🎧 Listen and check (✓).
07

1 Where was Kate yesterday?

a ☐   b ☐   c ☐

2 What was in the lake?

a ☐   b ☐   c ☐

3 Where were her parents?

a ☐   b ☐   c ☐

Word study: words you can count

4 Circle the words you can count.

bird　fish　frog　grass　hill
lake　meadow　pond　rock　sand

5 Read and write. Use the words from Activity 4.

1 four ....
2 ten ....
3 three ....
4 seven ....
5 three ....
6 two ....
7 five ....
8 four ....

160

Reading 1

1 Read *Great Outings* and match.

1　Lake Chapala is　　　　　　　　a　lakes and ponds.
2　Southern Cassowaries are　　　b　an enormous forest.
3　Pelicans live on　　　　　　　　c　trees.
4　Daintree is　　　　　　　　　　d　long and wide.
5　Some kangaroos live in　　　　e　rare birds.

2 Read *Great Outings* again and write.

1　What do pelicans look like?

　　..

2　Which places in North America do they fly from?

　　..

3　What wildlife can you see at Lake Chapala?

　　..

4　What kind of animals are Southern Cassowaries?

　　..

5　What can you do on an aerial walkway?

　　..

6　What's different about the hills in Daintree Forest?

　　..

3 Where do you like going on vacation? What do you like doing outdoors on vacation? Write and draw.

Grammar 1

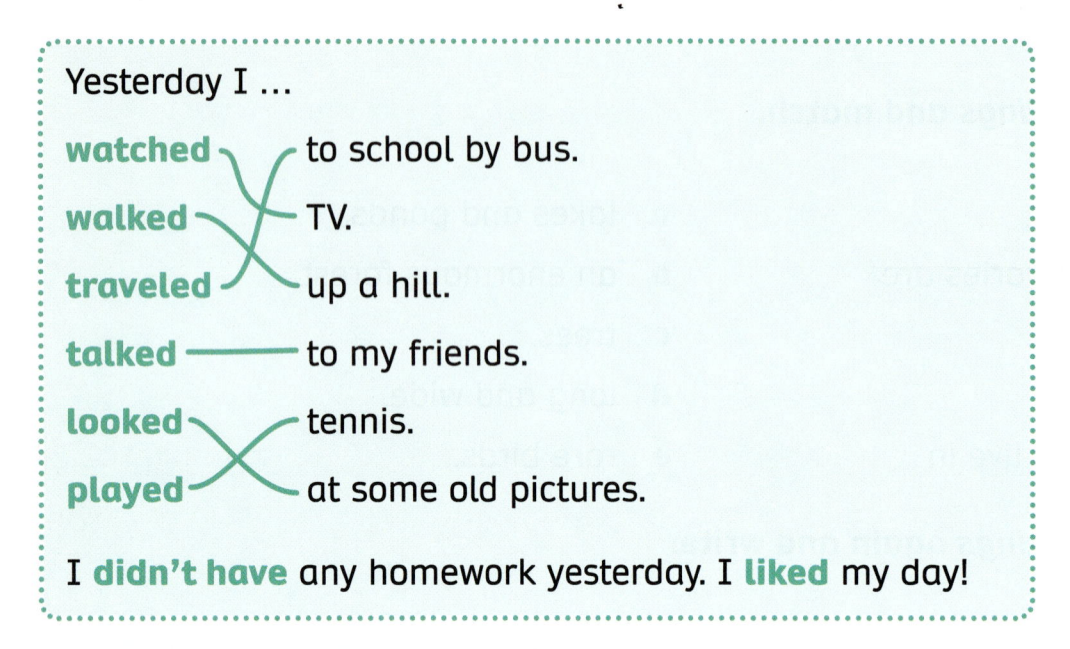

Yesterday I …

- watched — TV.
- walked — to school by bus.
- traveled — up a hill.
- talked — to my friends.
- looked — at some old pictures.
- played — tennis.

I **didn't have** any homework yesterday. I **liked** my day!

1 Read and match.

Yesterday …

1. we walked
2. you played
3. I cooked
4. Sally watched
5. it rained
6. the students listened

a. and snowed.
b. to school.
c. to the teacher.
d. soccer.
e. TV.
f. lunch.

2 Read and write what Anna did/didn't do yesterday.

1. She _cleaned_ the windows.
2. She _____ Mom's car.
3. She _____ Bobby.
4. She _____ Grandma.
5. She _____ tennis.
6. She _____ the dog.
7. She _____ her English homework.

Things to do today!

- Clean the windows ✓
- Wash Mom's car ✗
- Call Bobby ✓
- Visit Grandma ✓
- Play tennis ✗
- Walk the dog ✓
- Finish my English homework ✗

162

3 Look, choose, and write.

~~cook~~   look at   play   watch

1. I _cooked_ spaghetti.
   I _didn't cook_ fish.

3. I _____ the pictures in an album. I _____ the pictures on the wall.

2. The children _____ a video game. They _____ cards.

4. You _____ a movie on TV. You _____ soccer.

4 Choose and write about what you and your family or friends did/didn't do last weekend.

collect   cook   enjoy   play   travel   visit   walk   watch

Last weekend, we walked in the hills.
My father didn't cook breakfast. He cooked dinner.

Vocabulary 2

1 Look, read, and check (✓) or cross (✗).

1. These are fins. ☐
2. These are shells. ☐
3. This is a snorkel. ☐
4. This is a sandcastle. ☐
5. This is seaweed. ☐

2 Choose and write.

| air mattress | fins | sandcastle | seaweed | shells |
| snorkel | water wings |

In the ocean — air mattress — At the beach

164

3 Read and write the letters in order.

1. My sister wears *rewat gswni* _____ when she goes swimming.
2. I used a *klesnro* _____ to swim underwater.
3. We ate dried *eeewsda* _____ with some rice.
4. Gerry collected *ellshs* _____ at the beach.
5. Tommy and Fran won a competition for their amazing *anaesdlstc* _____ .
6. The diver wore *snif* _____ on his feet to help him swim fast.
7. They stayed in a five-star *teloh* _____ .
8. I relaxed on an *ira metstars* _____ in the swimming pool.

Vocabulary challenge: seaside

4 Look, choose, and write.

bridge   marina   pier   wave

1. _____
2. _____
3. _____
4. _____

5 Read and write. Use the words from Activity 4.

1. Look at this _____ ! Someone is surfing it!
2. This is a _____ where boats stay overnight.
3. Let's walk on this _____ to get to the other side of the river.
4. There are a lot of pelicans sitting on this _____ .

165

Reading 2

1
Read *Samira's Sea Glass Collection*. Check (✓) the things Samira and her family did on vacation.

1 Watched movies ☐
2 Went fishing ☐
3 Surfed ☐
4 Looked at birds ☐
5 Collected things ☐
6 Snorkeled ☐
7 Made sandcastles ☐
8 Walked in the hills ☐
9 Played on the sand ☐
10 Went swimming ☐

2
Read *Samira's Sea Glass Collection* again and write.

1 Samira and her family stayed in a small .... at the beach.
2 Samira helped her sister build ....
3 Samira and her brother loved .... in the ocean with their dad.
4 Samira collected driftwood, sea glass, ... , ... , and .... at the beach.
5 Samira decided to put the sea glass in a ....

3
Draw and color a sea glass heart. Label the colors and shapes.

Grammar 2

Did you stay in a hotel? **No**, I **didn't**.
Did she stay with your grandma? **Yes**, she **did**.

1 Read and match.

1 Did Katya swim in the ocean?
2 Did her brother swim with fins and a snorkel?
3 Did her parents stay in a hotel?
4 Did you see Katya at the beach, Luke?
5 Did you and Katya ride horses?

a Yes, we did.
b No, she didn't.
c Yes, he did.
d No, they didn't.
e Yes, I did.

2 Read and write.

1 Did you go to Australia? (✓)
Yes, I did.

2 Did you travel alone? (✗)
....

3 Did you and your friend sleep outdoors? (✓)
....

4 Did people help you? (✓)
....

5 Did you see a kangaroo? (✗)
....

6 Did your friends call you? (✗)
....

3 Write the words in order to make questions.

1 go / on / Did / last / vacation / you / summer

　...?

2 Did / your / you / in / and / family / stay / a / hotel

　...?

3 the / ocean / swim / Did / you / in

　...?

4 enjoy / your / you / vacation / Did

　...?

5 pictures / you / take / Did

　...?

6 with / you / your / go / grandparents / Did

　...?

4 Read Miguel's diary and write.

> My family went to the zoo today. I had a great time! I saw tigers, gorillas, and hippos. My favorite animal was a snake! My sister Lucy gave some food to a baby lamb, but I didn't. We had pizza for lunch. Lucy slept on the train home, but I didn't. I was too excited!

1 Did Miguel have fun at the zoo?
2 Did he see a camel?
3 Did Lucy give food to a baby lamb?
4 Did Miguel sleep on the train home?

5 Write for you.

1 Did you do your homework yesterday?
2 Did your dad cook dinner last night?
3 Did you play sports on the weekend?

Writing

1 Read, choose, and write.

> like a forest like a rabbit
> like a hotel   like pelicans

Remember
1 Read.
2 Get ready to write.
3 Now write!

1 The yard is ....
2 The kangaroo has long ears, ...
3 There were enormous white birds, ...
4 It's an enormous house, ...

2 Think about your favorite outdoor place. Read and write.

My Favorite Outdoor Place

1 Where is it?
....
2 What can you do there?
....
3 What can you see there?
....
4 Why do you like this outdoor place? Write the things you did and saw.
....

3 Draw and write about your favorite outdoor place. Use your answers from Activity 2.

169

Now I Know

1 Choose words from A and B and write new words.

A | air   sand   sea   water   wild |

B | castle   life   mattress   weed   wings |

1 ....
2 ....
3 ....
4 ....
5 ....

2 Look, read, and write.

1 What did/didn't Cathy pack for her vacation?

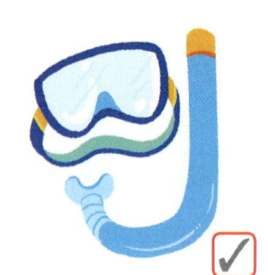

✓   ✓   ✓   ✗

She ...., ..., and
....
She .... her math book.

2 What did/didn't she collect at the beach?

✓   ✓   ✗

She .... and ....
She ....

170

3 Write questions and answers about last summer.

1 you / enjoy / your vacation

.... ?

Yes, ...

2 your brother / swim / in the ocean

.... ?

No, ...

3 you and your family / stay in a hotel

.... ?

Yes, ...

4 it / rain

.... ?

No, ...

Things I learn

1 What do you see and do outdoors? Write five words.

....

2 My new words! Draw and write.

3 My favorite words in this unit!

My three favorite words in this unit are ....

171

Pearson Education Limited
KAO TWO
KAO Park
Hockham Way
Harlow, Essex
CM17 9SR
England
and Associated Companies throughout the world.

www.English.com

© Pearson Education Limited 2019

The right of Cheryl Pelteret to be identified as author of this Work has been asserted by her in accordance with the Copyright, Designs and Patents Act 1988.

All rights reserved; no part of this publication may be reproduced, stored in a retrieval system, or transmitted in any form or by any means, electronic, mechanical, photocopying, recording, or otherwise without the prior written permission of the Publishers.

First published 2019

ISBN: 978-1-292-21943-1

Set in Daytona Pro Primary

Printed in Italy by L.E.G.O.

Image Credit(s):
123RF.com: Andersonrise 136, Andriy Popov 10, Astrid Gast 44, Avemario 89, Bloodua 165, Bonzami Emmanuelle 89, Cathy Yeulet 136, 78, 99, Chakrapong Worathat 47, Denis Radovanovic 89, Deusexlupus 75, Domenicogelermo 42, Elena Nichizhenova 106, Eric Isselee 105, Fedorkondratenko 154, Fotojagodka 141, Fotyma 123, Frescomovie 75, Goodluz 99, Ian Iankovskii 106, Igor Averin 128, Jedimaster 137, Jose Manuel Gelpi Diaz 99, Joseelias 109, Jovan Mandic 137, Kanyarat Bunnag 128, Kian Khoon Tan 10, Kittikhun Prakrajang 123, Kurhan 105, Leonid Tit 126, Lorena Nasi 30, Luca Bertolli 136, Lutai Razvan Alexandru 25, Lynne Albright 165, Maksym Topchii 78, Mattiaath 30, Mihtiander 154, Mishoo 34, 44, Monticello 95, Nalinratana Phiyanalinmat 95, Oksana Mironova 48, Oleg Elagin 25, Pauliene Wessel 109, Pavla Zakova 143, Sebastien Decoret 44, Sietevidas 160, Simon Dannhauer 127, Sung Kuk Kim 34, Susan Richey-Schmitz 75, Talanis 10, Tatyana Tomsickova 78, Vit Kovalcik 105, Vitalii Zaporozhets 29, Wavebreak Media Ltd 10, 106, 136, WavebreakMedia Ltd 5, Wavebreakmediamicro 139, Weedezign 160, Winai Tepsuttinun 95, Yobro10 108, Yod Pimsen 20, Yulia Kuznetsova 99, _ig0rzh_ 154, Дмитрий Сладков 75; **Alamy Stock Photo:** Andy Harmer 160, Bill Cheyrou 106, Brian Overcast 161, Catalin Petolea 38, ClassicStock 138, Cultura Creative (RF) 151, Ferenc Szelepcsenyi 47, 48, Gennadiy Poznyakov 64, Geoff Smith 10, Hero Images Inc 146, 48, Ian Allenden 5, ImageBROKER 44, Incamerastock 47, Joana Kruse 50, Juniors Bildarchiv GmbH 96 MITO images GmbH 13, Mauritius Images GmbH 43, Novarc Images 47, Paul Mayall Wildlife 23, Philipus 47, Prisma by Dukas Presseagentur GmbH 20, Radius Images 78, Roy Riley 108, Sergey Zaikov 44, Stephen Frink Collection 20, Stephen Mulcahey 75, Steve Skjold 67, Tetra Images 11, Tronin Konstantin 30, Veryan Dale 95; **BBC Worldwide Learning:** 102, 116, 130, 144, 158, 18, 32, 4, 46, 60, 74, 88; **Getty Images:** Alison Langley 81, Ariel Skelley/DigitalVision 67, Fstop123 16, Heide Benser 38, Hero Images 67, Jason Todd 38, Jose Luis Pelaez Inc/DigitalVision 68, Kristianbell 26, Robert Nicholas 47, SonerCdem 146, Soren Hald 81, Timsa 146, Vgajic 12; **Pearson Education:** Gareth Boden 48, 54, Jules Selmes 48, Studio 8 57, 6, Trevor Clifford 70; **Pearson Education Australia Pty Ltd:** Alice McBroom 5; **Shutterstock.com:** @erics 78, A3pfamily 154, Africa Studio 109, 5, 78, Andrey Armyagov 82, Andrey Skutin 44, Anothai Thiansawang 89, Artush 123, Artyme83 45, Auremar 81, Bart Sadowski 151, Boris Bulychev 106, Borislav Bajkic 95, Brian A Jackson 114, David Shawley 89, Djgis 160, Dotshock 47, Dr. J. Beller 105, Dr.Pixel 160, Ermolaev Alexander 106, Gary Yim 123, Gaschwald 26, Gladskikh Tatiana 9, Gpointstudio 5, Happy monkey 85, Hung Chung Chih 20, 42, Ilozavr 154, Jason Cox 95, Jim Lopes 34, Jiri Hera 109, KK Tan 145, LR_Perspective 154, Labutin.Art 154, Lee Yiu Tung 30, Levent Konuk 109, Lindsay Douglas 160, LineTale 154, Littlekidmoment 11, Longjourneys 165, Lopolo 9, Losevsky Pavel 108, Lucky Business 67, LumineImages 76, Maradon 333 128, Marcovarro 81, MariMarkina 30, Maria Skaldina 154, Martin Novak 5, Matthieu Gallet 26, Maxim van Asseldonk 44, Michael Potter11 31, Mila May 108, Minerva Studio 34, Monkey Business Images 54, Naluwan 151, Nebojsa Markovic 44, Neelsky 30, OZaiachin 75, Olaf Naami 34, OlegD 47, Ollirg 165, Ondrej Prosicky 20, Pakhnyushcha 143, Photo One 111, Photodonato 53, Photoiva 139, Pichugin Dmitry 20, Pitchayarat Chootai 53, Ralf Geithe 146, Rawpixel.com 151, Richie Chan 53, Rick Partington 75, Rostislav_Sedlacek 128, Satyrenko 12, Sheff 48, Siam.pukkato 53, Sirikorn Thamniyom 64, Soloviova Liudmyla 108, Steve Heap 160, Stockfour 136, Stone36 126, Sukharevskyy Dmytro 111, Swa182 34, Syda Productions 118, Sylv1rob1 75, Tammykayphoto 89, Tatjana Romanova 45, The Len 25, Tom Wang 10, Tracy Whiteside 136, Tyler Olson 76, VictoriaKh 111, Vladyslav Starozhylov 160, Voronin76 108, Vovan 109, Wavebreakmedia 11, 137, 71, Wizdata 53, Yuda Chen 25, Yuganov Konstantin 36, Yulia Davidovich 111, Yuriy Kulik 160, rShapshotPhotos 53.

Cover Images: *Front:* **Getty Images:** Cavan Images

Illustrated by Marta Alvarez Miguens (Astound) p. 21; Nila Aye (Meiklejohn) p. 14, 16, 23, 27, 35, 41, 42, 44, 52, 55(t), 62, 86, 92, 104, 107, 117, 121, 134, 137, 145, 147, 148(t), 150, 164, 165, 168, 170; Beatrice Blue (The Bright Agency) p. 133; The Boy Fitz Hammond (NB Illustration) p. 49; Camilla Galindo (Beehive Illustration) p. 48, 91, 94, 100, 112, 119(t), 124, 125, 132, 135, 142, 159, 163, 167; Francesca Gambatesa (MMB Creative) p. 5, 6, 24, 38, 39, 51, 58, 65, 66, 80, 93, 97, 98, 103, 110, 112, 128, 140, 148; Rebecca Gibbon (illustration Web) p. 40; Desideria Guicciardini (Milan Illustrations Agency) p. 91; Lisa Hunt (The Bright Agency) p. 77; John Lund (Beehive Illustration) p. 63; Jem Maybank (The Bright Agency) p. 166 Alex Patrick (The Bright Agency) p. 152 Sussana Rumiz (Lemonade Illustration) p. 16, 19, 21, 22, 29, 33, 36, 37, 50, 55, 56, 61, 71, 73, 87, 124; Richard Smythe (The Bright Agency) p. 119; Richard Watson (The Bright Agency) p. 7, 8.